EQUILIBRIUM
STATISTICAL
MECHANICS

EQUILIBRIUM STATISTICAL MECHANICS

FRANK C. ANDREWS

Department of Chemistry
University of Wisconsin

JOHN WILEY & SONS, INC.
NEW YORK · LONDON · SYDNEY

Library of Congress Catalog Card Number: 63-22204
Printed in the United States of America

TO MY PARENTS

PREFACE

As times change, the demands on students of science and technology increase. They must know more and more at ever earlier stages of their education. Scientists and engineers have long recognized the need for good training in such subjects as thermodynamics and the properties of materials. During the twentieth century, as more fundamental thinking has invaded these disciplines, the study of the molecular structure of matter has assumed greater emphasis compared to the macroscopic studies. For example, thermodynamics alone is seen as inadequate for today's undergraduate or graduate student, unless he is at least introduced to the mechanics of the atoms and molecules which gives rise to the observable phenomena of thermodynamics.

This, then, is the problem of statistical mechanics—*to rationalize the macroscopic behavior of matter through the knowledge that matter is composed of discrete particles.* Rarely is there time in the busy curriculum for a course in nothing but statistical mechanics. Bits of it arise in courses on mechanics, physical chemistry, thermodynamics, properties of materials, fluid mechanics, solid state electronics, and who knows how many others. Because of limitations in time, suitable books, and faculty training and interests, it is hard for students to come to grips with statistical mechanics to even the following extent:

1. To understand what statistical mechanics attempts to do, the method by which it proposes to do this, and the "truth" or "falsehood" of its results.

2. To understand the basic tools of statistical mechanics. Like the tools of thermodynamics—energy and entropy—those of statistical mechanics are not easily grasped at first. But they are vital in comprehending the subject.

3. Using these tools, to study some of their simpler applications. This work often goes under such names as "the kinetic theory of matter" and "statistical thermodynamics." It gives insight into some

of the "why's" of thermodynamics and the properties of materials. It also helps a person see other ways to use statistical mechanics in his own thinking and work.

4. To do all the above within a framework of definitions and viewpoints which is directly capable of being extended without any demolition all the way out to the frontiers of statistical mechanical research.

These four points represent my goal in writing this book. There is no wonder that reaching this goal has been hard for both students and teachers, because even today there is not much agreement among professional statistical mechanicians (a singularly quarrelsome bunch) on many of these points. If I have discarded cherished approaches and substituted others, it is because to me the substituted ones make more sense. I have tried only to reach the goal in a way which seems clear.

The methods of statistical mechanics are applied to a variety of problems. Such unity as the subject has comes from its dependence on the basic principles, given in Part I of this book. Throughout the entire book, the emphasis is on understanding the fundamentals. The problems that are scattered throughout (with their hints and answers at the back) have been picked to illustrate topics discussed in the text, to present applications, and to encourage independent thinking and understanding. They are a very important part of the book. The first twenty or twenty-one sections comprise the elementary part of the subject.

The amount of background assumed for the reader is that usually given by general chemistry, physics, and calculus courses, and by any survey of thermodynamics, such as is given in undergraduate physical chemistry and many undergraduate engineering courses. No quantum mechanics is needed, although such quantum mechanical conclusions as energy levels and quantum states are introduced without apology. Most students run into this much quantum mechanics in their first year or two in college. Others may just have to "buy" these results and see how statistical mechanics uses them.

I hope the reader enjoys this book and its subject. Statistical mechanics has appealed to so many of the great minds of the past hundred years— Joule, Rayleigh, Clausius, Maxwell, Boltzmann, Kelvin, Gibbs, Planck, Einstein, von Neumann, Dirac, Fermi, Debye—just to name a few! The reader of this book should never feel, however, that he is reading a gospel. But that is true for any student of the sciences, as well as of the humanities, or even life itself. We must each make our own order out of the welter of ideas and facts we find ourselves in. In doing this we have the heritage from all those who have gone before to guide us. For here we are reaching, however hesitantly, toward that goal of scientific theory—*to show the logical necessity of the behavior of the physical world from as simple a set of basic assumptions as possible.*

ACKNOWLEDGMENTS

I wish to thank the National Science Foundation for a grant which facilitated the writing of this book. I also thank the many friends whose comments helped clarify fuzzy points, in particular, R. B. Bird and C. F. Curtiss. For valuable creative reviews of the manuscript I am indebted to J. E. Mayer and D. R. Herschbach.

Madison, Wisconsin   FRANK C. ANDREWS
September 1963

CONTENTS

PART III—SPECIAL TOPICS 131

APPENDICES 187

INDEX 203

EQUILIBRIUM
STATISTICAL
MECHANICS

PART I

BASIC THEORY

I | INTRODUCTION

Most of the physical phenomena studied by scientists and engineers during the entire history of science are what are called *macroscopic* phenomena. That is, they involve matter in bulk, say, a chunk of metal, a beaker of liquid, or a tank of gas. Nevertheless, during the past hundred years, scientists have come to believe that all matter is composed of molecules made of atoms; and that it is these molecules, interacting among themselves according to some force laws or other, which in their enormous number give rise to the macroscopic, observable phenomena we see.

It is hard to realize that this microscopic picture we all take for granted is really only a century old. True, it had been cropping up among philosophic writings for two thousand years, but its general acceptance by the scientific community came only in the latter half of the nineteenth century. Its acceptance arose from the same cause as that of most good theories—from the scientist's desire to unify and make order out of the endless phenomena about him by showing that they all would follow logically if certain simple hypotheses were true. Certainly, one of the most successful of such creations of the scientific community is the molecular hypothesis, which has tied together so many previously unrelated theories and phenomena and led to so many remarkable new realms of study and technology.

Now, since the molecular theory makes sense, it should be possible to show that a vast number of molecules rattling around and bumping into each other at appropriate intervals would indeed produce the macroscopic phenomena we see. The motion of all these molecules should, of course, be describable by the known mechanical laws. Before 1900 the study was limited to classical mechanics. The development of quantum mechanics during the period 1901 to 1926 brought greater precision to the description.

The magnitude of the many-particle problem posed by macroscopic objects can be appreciated by realizing just how many molecules are believed to be in a mole of any substance. If each molecule in a mole were the size of a small dried pea, there would be enough peas to cover the United States to a depth of several hundred feet. When we consider that in either quantum or classical mechanics it has proved impossible to solve the equations which give the trajectories of *just three* mutually interacting bodies, the problem here, involving 6×10^{23} bodies, seems almost laughable. In fact, if we just wrote down the x, y, and z coordinates of each molecule a thousand to the page and a thousand per minute, it would take a million times as long to write them as the estimated age of the earth, and a freight train loaded with the pages would stretch to the sun and back about 40,000 times!

How, then, might this problem be tackled? It has been a long, hard process even to get a language and a reasonable means of approach, and that process is still going on. What has developed is a mixture of mechanical and probabilistic arguments called *statistical mechanics*. It is vitally important to understand what is mechanics and what is probability in order to interpret the results of this branch of science. Confusion between these arguments and the assumptions involved in them has resulted in a century of misconceptions and quarrels. Nevertheless, the first successes of statistical mechanics hastened the general acceptance of the molecular theory by the scientific community. Since that time, continuing successes have shed great light on countless physical phenomena.

The physicists whose successes established the foundations of statistical mechanics in the scientific world were J. Clerk Maxwell of Cambridge and Ludwig Boltzmann of Vienna. These two did their major work between approximately 1860 and 1900. The entire field was carefully studied by J. Willard Gibbs of Yale, whose brilliant synthesis and creative exposition published in 1902 brought order and stability to the foundations laid by Maxwell and Boltzmann. The work has progressed with much debate and controversy to the present. Still, we must always be impressed by the great insight of Gibbs into the fundamentals of the subject, an insight prevented from complete success only by the fact that the full development of quantum mechanics was still twenty-five years in the future.

2   THERMODYNAMICS VERSUS STATISTICAL MECHANICS

It is important to understand the difference between thermodynamics and statistical mechanics. Thermodynamics deals with matter in bulk, that is, with macroscopic objects. It starts with certain basic postulates called the "laws of thermodynamics," and from these and some other hypotheses and experimental facts derives relationships between the observed properties of substances. Thermodynamics does not try to explain through mechanics *why* a substance has the properties it does. The job of thermodynamics is *to link together the many observable properties of macroscopic objects*, so that knowledge of a few will permit calculation of many others. The "truth" of thermodynamics rests in its never failing to give valid answers to problems involving macroscopic systems.*

Except perhaps in discussing the third law, thermodynamics takes no account of the atomic and molecular structure of matter. However, the causal "explanation" of the laws of thermodynamics must lie in the mechanics of the particles comprising the macroscopic system. One could present statistical mechanics in such a way as to "derive" the laws of thermodynamics. Using this approach, one might step back and exclaim, "Look, we have just derived the second law of thermodynamics!" No such approach is taken here. The laws of thermodynamics are valid and assumed known. Their formulation from statistical mechanics sheds light on their meaning and ranges of validity. It does not make them any more "true." It is, however, gratifying that the assumptions on which statistical mechanics is grounded contain the thermodynamic laws as consequences. Of course, if it were otherwise, the assumptions would long ago have been changed.

Statistical mechanics may be viewed as the discipline which bridges the gap between the microscopic world of molecules, atoms, and fundamental particles and the macroscopic world of thermodynamics and the properties of materials. Given a picture of the microscopic world, statistical mechanics sets out to determine what macroscopic behavior to expect. Sometimes the macroscopic properties enable statistical mechanics to shed light on the microscopic picture causing them.

---

* For further discussion, see Pippard, Chap. 1.

The validity of the macroscopic results of statistical mechanics depends on the accuracy of the microscopic picture used. Primarily, it is mathematical difficulties that keep statistical mechanics from giving quantitative *descriptions* of most macroscopic phenomena. On the other hand, thermodynamics as a discipline is unaffected by any microscopic picture. In consequence, it is limited to *relating* the results of one set of measurements to another. In practice it is important for a person to keep a clear picture of which conclusions about his problem have thermodynamic validity and which follow from statistical mechanics. For this reason, the author believes that thermodynamics and statistical mechanics should be studied as two separate disciplines. They may be studied concurrently, each shedding light on the other; but one is a purely macroscopic study, the other a bridge between the macroscopic world and the microscopic.

3   THE PROBLEM OF STATISTICAL MECHANICS

The problem to which statistical mechanics addresses itself is basically the same for both equilibrium and non-equilibrium conditions. One has a system in the sense of thermodynamics: *A system is that part of the physical world to which one directs his attention.* Furthermore, he has a microscopic picture of the system. This means knowledge of the mechanical behavior of the constituent particles, whatever they may be—molecules, atoms, ions, electrons, or photons. This information is furnished by such microscopic disciplines as molecular quantum mechanics, spectroscopy, x-ray crystallography, and the physics of fundamental particles.

Certain macroscopic information is also known about the system as a result of some macroscopic measurements. It may be a minimum; for example, the volume, the number and type of particles, and the fact that they are "in equilibrium at a given temperature" or "in equilibrium with a given energy." Or it may be very extensive and detailed information characterizing a system that is about to evolve in some complicated non-equilibrium process. In the discussion that follows this macroscopic information is called the *initial information*.

The problem of statistical mechanics is to compute the probabilities of the various possible results of other measurements one might choose to make on the system. The computation involves finding how the initial information and the known mechanical behavior of the constituent particles affect various other measurements. These other measurements might be made at the same time the initial information is taken. Or, if the system is "in equilibrium" time will not even be a factor in the problem. Or, the other measurements might be made at a later time after the system, in this case non-equilibrium, has evolved for a while.

One can only compute *probabilities* of various results of other measurements. For most macroscopic measurements, however, the tremendous number of particles involved gives rise to a great simplification. The most probable result of a measurement proves to be overwhelmingly probable. Significant deviations from it have only vanishing probabilities. This means that once statistical mechanics has found this overwhelmingly likely result of a measurement, it may be safely predicted that this result is the one which will be found in the system. Therefore, the calculated values of properties like pressure and density given by statistical mechanics are usually these most probable values. This procedure is justified and discussed in Sec. 33.

Whether or not a particular result of a macroscopic measurement is overwhelmingly probable, the problem of statistical mechanics still is to give the relative probabilities of all possible results. Clearly, it is necessary to phrase statistical mechanics in the language of probability theory. In order to do this, one must understand the theory of probability, first of all quite in the abstract and divorced from physical content. This may make dull reading, but the points discussed should come to life later in their physical context. It is very important, however, to know which parts of statistical mechanics arise from the physics and which parts simply from the mathematical language of probability theory.

4   ELEMENTS OF PROBABILITY THEORY

The theory of probability is a well-defined branch of mathematics. Like any other branch of mathematics, it is a self-consistent way of defining and thinking about certain idealizations. When it is used by the scientist, it becomes no more than a logical method of thinking—of examining the consequences of a set of assumptions. To the scientist mathematics is simply one of his logical tools—broadly speaking, the logic of quantity. Whenever in science mathematical conclusions seem unbelievable, it just means that the assumptions must be modified so they no longer imply the objectionable conclusions.

In this section we consider the language of probability theory, in which statistical mechanics is expressed. We parallel the formal discussion with a simple example in smaller print, to lend substance to the formal presentation.

Probability theory treats the properties of a completely abstract idealization we call an ensemble. *An **ensemble** is a collection of members, each of which has certain characteristics.* Depending on the problem, there may be just a few members, many members, or an infinite number of members.

Consider as an ensemble a certain hypothetical collection of cats. Each cat has certain characteristics—color, sex, age, number of teeth, weight, length. *Note:* Color and sex are certain qualities that characterize each cat. Age (since last birthday) and number of teeth are parameters that take only discrete values. Weight and length are continuous parameters characterizing the cats.

The **probability** P of a certain characteristic is defined by the following equation:

$$P(\text{characteristic}) = \frac{\text{number of members of ensemble with characteristic}}{\text{total number of members of ensemble}}$$

$$(4\text{-}1)$$

If the characteristic of interest is labeled i, then Eq. 4-1 may be rewritten in the obvious notation

$$P(i) \equiv \frac{n(i)}{n}.$$

$$(4\text{-}2)$$

The probability of characteristic i is simply the fraction of members of the ensemble that possess characteristic i. While Eq. 4-1 may agree with our intuitive ideas about the likelihood of selecting a member at random from the ensemble and finding it to possess characteristic i, this is less important than the fact that the *mathematical definition* of probability is given by Eq. 4-1 or 4-2.

The probability of a male cat is defined as the number of male cats in the ensemble divided by the total number of cats.

Most of the mathematical properties of probabilities follow directly from Eq. 4-2—

If characteristic i appears in no members of the ensemble, its probability is zero:

$$P(i) = \frac{n(i)}{n} = \frac{0}{n} = 0. \tag{4-3}$$

If characteristic i appears in all members of the ensemble, its probability is unity:

$$P(i) = \frac{n(i)}{n} = \frac{n}{n} = 1. \tag{4-4}$$

If all cats in the ensemble are alive, the probability of a dead cat is zero. The probability of a living cat is unity.

Consider characteristics i and j to be mutually exclusive. This means that no member of the ensemble has both i and j. Then, the probability of finding *either* characteristic i *or* characteristic j is $P(i)$ plus $P(j)$:

$$P(i \text{ or } j) = \frac{n(i) + n(j)}{n} = P(i) + P(j). \tag{4-5}$$

If no cat is both yellow and black, the characteristics of yellow and black color are mutually exclusive. In that case, the probability of a cat's being either yellow or black is the probability of a yellow one plus the probability of a black one.

If $P(i)$ is the probability of characteristic i, then $1 - P(i)$ is the probability of *not* finding characteristic i:

$$P(\text{not } i) = \frac{n(\text{not } i)}{n} = \frac{n - n(i)}{n} = 1 - P(i). \tag{4-6}$$

DISCRETE PARAMETERS

For the moment, consider only characteristics that are represented by a number; that is, consider some parameter that takes on discrete values. Assume that *each* member of the ensemble has *some* value of this parameter. This will always be the case in the use of probability theory in statistical mechanics. The allowed values of the ith characteristic are given the symbol l_i. The probability that characteristic i has the value l_i is simply

$$P_i(l_i) = \frac{n(l_i)}{n}. \tag{4-7}$$

Since no member of the ensemble can have two different values of the parameter, the condition of mutual exclusiveness is satisfied automatically for the validity of Eq. 4-5.

A simple extension of Eq. 4-5 is the following: *The sum of* $P_i(l_i)$ *over all possible values* l_i *of the parameter yields unity:*

$$\sum_{l_i} P_i(l_i) = \sum_{l_i} \frac{n(l_i)}{n} = \frac{n}{n} = 1. \tag{4-8}$$

A probability that satisfies Eq. 4-8 is said to be **normalized**, and Eq. 4-8 is often called the **normalization condition**.

> Each cat is characterized by some unique value of its age. Therefore, the probability of either a 2 year old or a 3 year old cat is the sum of the individual probabilities. Furthermore, the sum of the probabilities over all the possible ages must yield unity, since it includes all cats in the ensemble.

Each member of the ensemble is characterized by some value l_i of parameter i. If one were to compute the value of any function of l_i, say, $g(l_i)$, for each member of the ensemble and find the average of all these values, his result would be the **ensemble average** of g, which is written $\bar{g}$. The formula for finding $\bar{g}$ from the probabilities P_i is easily obtained from the definition of the average of a set of numbers as the sum of the numbers divided by the number of numbers:

$$\bar{g} = \frac{1}{n} \sum_{\substack{\text{all members} \\ \text{of ensemble}}} g(\text{member})$$

$$= \frac{1}{n} \sum_{\substack{\text{all possible} \\ \text{values of } l_i}} n[g(l_i)]g(l_i)$$

$$= \frac{1}{n} \sum_{l_i} n(l_i)g(l_i),$$

$$\boxed{\bar{g} = \sum_{l_i} P_i(l_i)g(l_i).} \tag{4-9}$$

Each cat has an age l. Consider the function l^2. The average value of l^2 for the cats in the ensemble is the "ensemble average of l^2," written $\overline{l^2}$. To calculate $\overline{l^2}$ one simply multiplies l^2 times $P(l)$ for each l and sums this product over all possible ages l.

Once the ensemble average of g is found, the amount by which $g(l_i)$ differs from the mean may be computed for any value of l_i and given the symbol $\delta g(l_i)$:

$$g(l_i) - \bar{g} \equiv \delta g(l_i). \tag{4-10}$$

The ensemble average of the deviation from the mean is of course zero:

$$\overline{\delta g} = \sum_{l_i} P_i(l_i)[g(l_i) - \bar{g}]$$

$$= \sum_{l_i} P_i(l_i)g(l_i) - \bar{g} \sum_{l_i} P_i(l_i),$$

$$\overline{\delta g} = \bar{g} - \bar{g} = 0, \tag{4-11}$$

which arises from the definition of the average. The mean positive deviation from the average exactly cancels the mean negative deviation from it.

If one seeks a useful measure of the average deviation of $g(l_i)$ from its mean value, the signs of positive and negative deviations must be omitted somehow so they will not cancel. A simple and useful way to accomplish this is to average the square of $\delta g(l_i)$:

$$\overline{\delta g^2} = \sum_{l_i} P_i(l_i)[g(l_i) - \bar{g}]^2$$

$$= \sum_{l_i} P_i(l_i)[g(l_i)^2 - 2g(l_i)\bar{g} + \bar{g}^2]$$

$$= \overline{g^2} - 2\bar{g}^2 + \bar{g}^2,$$

$$\overline{\delta g^2} = \overline{g^2} - \bar{g}^2. \tag{4-12}$$

The left-hand side of Eq. 4-12 is positive unless $\delta g(l_i)$ is zero for all l_i. In that case, $g(l_i)$ would have the same constant value $\bar{g}$ for all l_i. For any other function g the average of its square will always be greater than the square of its average because, in averaging the squares, greater weight is given to the larger contributions.

Suppose the ensemble contained only four cats, aged 3, 6, 7, and 9. The ensemble average age is 25/4 or 6.25 years. The average deviation from the mean is $(-3.25 - 0.25 + 0.75 + 2.75)/4 = 0$. The mean square deviation, however, is $[(3.25)^2 + (0.25)^2 + (0.75)^2 + (2.75)^2]/4 = 4.69$, which is identical to $(3^2 + 6^2 + 7^2 + 9^2)/4 - (6.25)^2$.

The ensemble establishes a value of $P_i(l_i)$ for each possible value of the parameter l_i. Viewed in this way, $P_i(l_i)$ is a *function* of the value of the parameter l_i in the usual sense of the word: $P_i(l_i)$ *is a **function** of* l_i *if for every allowed value of* l_i *a unique value of* $P_i(l_i)$ *is implied.*

Suppose that each member of the ensemble is completely described by s different characteristics which are given by the values of a set of s parameters. If the characteristics are numbered $1, 2, 3, \ldots, i, \ldots, s$, the values of the respective parameters are $l_1, l_2, l_3, \ldots, l_i, \ldots, l_s$. Such an ensemble not only defines the simple one-parameter probabilities of Eq. 4-7, but it also defines so-called *joint probabilities*. The **joint probability** P_{ij} that not only the parameter representing characteristic i is l_i but also the parameter representing characteristic j is l_j is defined as follows: It is the fraction of members of the ensemble for which not only i has the value l_i but also j has the value l_j:

$$P_{ij}(l_i, l_j) = \frac{n(l_i \text{ and } l_j)}{n}. \tag{4-13}$$

The joint two-parameter probability P_{ij} is a function of the values of the two parameters l_i and l_j.

> The joint probability that a cat of age 5 has 18 teeth is the fraction of cats in the ensemble which are both 5 years old and have 18 teeth. The structure of the ensemble establishes such a probability as a function of age and number of teeth for all possible values of the two parameters.

Consider the formal relationship between $P_{ij}(l_i, l_j)$ and $P_i(l_i)$. How would one obtain $P_i(l_i)$ from $P_{ij}(l_i, l_j)$? In $P_i(l_i)$ as given by Eq. 4-7, the $n(l_i)$ of the numerator is the number of members of the ensemble for which parameter i has the value l_i. It makes no difference what value parameter j has; all values of parameter j contribute to $n(l_i)$ so long as parameter i has the value l_i. One may think of $n(l_i)$ as the sum of $n(l_i$ and $l_j)$ over *all possible* values of l_j:

$$n(l_i) = \sum_{l_j} n(l_i \text{ and } l_j). \tag{4-14}$$

Therefore, $P_i(l_i)$ may be found from $P_{ij}(l_i, l_j)$:

$$P_i(l_i) = \frac{n(l_i)}{n} = \frac{1}{n} \sum_{l_j} n(l_i \text{ and } l_j),$$

$$P_i(l_i) = \sum_{l_j} P_{ij}(l_i, l_j). \tag{4-15}$$

Knowledge of $P_{ij}(l_i, l_j)$ as a function of l_i and l_j is thus enough to find $P_i(l_i)$, and, by the analogous equation, $P_j(l_j)$:

$$P_j(l_j) = \sum_{l_i} P_{ij}(l_i, l_j). \tag{4-16}$$

The simple probability that a cat is 5 years old is just the fraction of cats of age 5. Finding this probability has nothing to do with the cat's teeth. If one likes, however, he may view the total number of 5 year old cats as the sum of the number of cats age 5 with 0 teeth, plus the number age 5 with 1 tooth, plus the number age 5 with 2 teeth, ... The probability that a cat is age 5 is identical to the sum of the joint probability of age 5 and some number of teeth over all possible numbers of teeth.

The ideas of Eqs. 4-15 and 4-16 are much used. The probabilities P_i and P_j are said to be of *lower order* than joint probabilities like P_{ij} which contain them. More information about the ensemble is provided by knowing P_{ij} as a function of l_i and l_j than by knowing P_i as a function of l_i and P_j as a function of l_j separately. The process of obtaining a lower order probability from one of higher order, as in Eqs. 4-15 and 4-16, is often called *reducing* the higher order probability, and the lower order probabilities thus obtained are called **reduced probabilities**. This is a different usage of the word "reduced" from that sometimes employed in referring to dimensionless variables, calling them "reduced variables."

In the event that s different parameters completely describe each member of the ensemble, the ultimate in joint probabilities is the probability that the first parameter has the value l_1 *and* the second has the value l_2 *and* the third has the value l_3 *and* . . . *and* the sth the value l_s:

$$P_{1,2,3,\ldots,s}(l_1, l_2, \ldots, l_s) = \frac{n(l_1 \text{ and } l_2 \text{ and } \ldots \text{ and } l_s)}{n}. \tag{4-17}$$

The joint probability given by Eq. 4-17 is sometimes called the **complete probability** for the ensemble. It is a function of *all* the s parameters which describe a member of the ensemble. If it is known as a function of the parameters, then one has *complete* knowledge of the ensemble. That is, he knows the relative magnitudes of the numerator of Eq. 4-17 for all possible combinations of values of the s parameters. This enables him to construct a replica of the ensemble completely, since the relative number of members of each type is known.

Quite evidently, all other probabilities relating to the ensemble may be formed by reducing the complete probability. In particular,

$$P_i(l_i) = \sum_{l_1} \sum_{l_2} \cdots \sum_{l_s} P_{1,2,3,\ldots,s}(l_1, l_2, \ldots, l_s). \tag{4-18}$$
$$\text{(excluding } l_i)$$

In words, Eq. 4-18 means that in counting members of the ensemble in order to find the numerator of Eq. 4-7, one pays no attention to the values of any of the parameters other than i. If parameter i has the value l_i, then that member of the ensemble contributes to the numerator, whatever values the other parameters may have.

Suppose that a cat were characterized by only its age and number of teeth. Then if one knew the joint probability as a function of age and number of teeth, he would have full knowledge of the ensemble. He would know the relative number of cats in the ensemble with every possible combination of age and number of teeth. He could find the simple probability of age by summing over all numbers of teeth and vice versa. Nothing else would have meaning in such an ensemble.

Characteristics i and j are said to be explicitly **correlated** whenever the structure of the function $P_i(l_i)$ varies with the value of l_j. The characteristics are **uncorrelated**, then, whenever $P_i(l_i)$ is independent of l_j. This means that $P_i(l_i)$ is the same function of l_i if figured from the complete ensemble as it is if figured from an ensemble composed of only those members with a particular value of l_j. That is, if i and j are uncorrelated,

$$P_i(l_i) = \frac{n(l_i)}{n} = \frac{n(l_i \text{ and } l_j)}{n(l_j)} \quad \text{for all values of } l_i \text{ and } l_j. \quad (4\text{-}19)$$

In Prob. 4-2, it is proved that Eq. 4-19 implies the analogous equation

$$P_j(l_j) = \frac{n(l_j)}{n} = \frac{n(l_j \text{ and } l_i)}{n(l_i)}. \quad (4\text{-}20)$$

If characteristics i and j are uncorrelated, P_i and P_j are said to be *independent* probabilities.

Two characteristics i and j may be independent even when $P_i(l_i)$ and $P_j(l_j)$ both depend on the value of some third parameter. In fact, even if i and j have a common cause which *implies* coupling between the values l_i and l_j, Eq. 4-19 is satisfied so long as explicit knowledge of l_j does not change the probability distribution for l_i.

As a result of the definition of uncorrelated characteristics, it follows that if i and j are uncorrelated, then the joint probability P_{ij} is the product of P_i and P_j:

$$P_{ij}(l_i \text{ and } l_j) = \frac{n(l_i \text{ and } l_j)}{n} = \frac{n(l_i)}{n} \cdot \frac{n(l_i \text{ and } l_j)}{n(l_i)}$$

$$= \frac{n(l_i)}{n} \cdot \frac{n(l_j)}{n} = P_i(l_i) \cdot P_j(l_j). \quad (4\text{-}21)$$

In science, the joint probabilities of independent characteristics are made to factor. All the dependence of the joint probability on each characteristic is contained in its own term in the product. If characteristics are not independent, their correlation prevents factoring the joint probability in such a way as to separate its dependence on the various characteristics.

If the number of teeth a cat had were completely independent of the cat's age, then one would expect the probability for age and the probability for teeth to be independent of each other. The joint probability would factor. Clearly, this is not the case as old cats are likely to have fewer teeth. Therefore, these characteristics are correlated, and the joint probability does not factor.

CONTINUOUS PARAMETERS

When one or more characteristics of the members of the ensemble are given by continuous parameters, the problem is slightly different. Continuous parameters may have any one of an infinite number of values, and the ensemble may be chosen to have an infinite number of members. This need not be alarming, even though Eq. 4-7 has infinity in the denominator. The feature of interest in the continuous case is not the probability that parameter i has some particular value x_i but the probability that it lies *between* two values x_i and $x_i + \Delta x_i$. This probability is simply defined as the fraction of members of the ensemble that have this parameter between x_i and $x_i + \Delta x_i$. Even with n infinite, this fraction is well defined.

The number of members for which the value of the parameter lies between x_i and $x_i + \Delta x_i$ is a function of both x_i and the interval. If one shrinks the interval Δx_i to an infinitesimal value dx_i, the probability may be used to define a **probability density** f_i:

$$\frac{n(\text{between } x_i \text{ and } x_i + dx_i)}{n} = f_i(x_i)\, dx_i. \tag{4-22}$$

The probability density f_i is simply the density of members of the ensemble, at a given value of x_i, divided by the total number of members. It is defined formally as

$$f_i(x_i) = \lim_{\Delta x_i \to 0} \left[\frac{n(\text{between } x_i \text{ and } x_i + \Delta x_i)}{n\, \Delta x_i} \right]. \tag{4-23}$$

In terms of f_i, the probability that parameter i lies between x_i and $x_i + \Delta x_i$ is given by the integral

$$P_i(\text{between } x_i \text{ and } x_i + \Delta x_i) = \int_{x_i}^{x_i + \Delta x_i} f_i(x_i')\, dx_i'. \tag{4-24}$$

The equations involving discrete parameters may be taken over directly into the continuous case if the summations are replaced by integrations. In particular, the probability density must be normalized to unity, as in Eq. 4-8:

$$\int f_i(x_i)\, dx_i = 1, \tag{4-25}$$

where the integral is over all allowed values of x_i. Also, the ensemble average of any function of x_i is found by the equation analogous to 4-9:

$$\bar{g} = \int g(x_i) f_i(x_i)\, dx_i, \tag{4-26}$$

where again the integral is over all allowed values of x_i.

It is frequently convenient to normalize f_i to something other than unity. If it were properly called a "probability density," the normalization would have to be to unity. Therefore, when f_i is normalized to something else, it is commonly called a **distribution function,** perhaps because it shows how the values of the parameter are "distributed" among the members of the ensemble. "Distribution functions" may be viewed as a general term embracing all different normalizations employed. In this book, any distribution functions used will be normalized to unity.

The number of cats whose length lies between L and $L + dL$ is simply the density of cats in the ensemble with length L (in units of cats/length) times dL. The probability that a cat has length between L and $L + dL$ is the number of such cats divided by the total number in the ensemble n. The density divided by n may be called the probability density for length of cats $f_L(L)$. Then $f_L(L)\, dL$ is the probability a cat's length lies between L and $L + dL$. The probability that a cat has length between any two values L_1 and L_2 is simply the integral

$$P(L_1 \leqslant L \leqslant L_2) = \int_{L_1}^{L_2} f_L(L)\, dL.$$

Higher order distribution functions or probability densities are defined similarly to higher order probabilities. For example, the probability that parameter i lies between x_i and $x_i + dx_i$ and that parameter j lies between x_j and $x_j + dx_j$ is simply $f_{ij}(x_i, x_j)\, dx_i\, dx_j$. Other higher order distribution functions may be defined in like fashion, all the way out to the complete distribution function, which gives information about all the parameters that characterize a member of the ensemble.

Lower order distribution functions may be obtained from those of higher order by integration, in analogy with Eqs. 4-15 and 4-16:*

$$f_i(x_i) = \int dx_j f_{ij}(x_i, x_j); \tag{4-27}$$

$$f_j(x_j) = \int dx_i f_{ij}(x_i, x_j). \tag{4-28}$$

---

* In this book it is common to find each differential immediately behind its integral instead of after the integrand. This is useful in multiple integrals in which the different variables have different limits. It emphasizes the variable over which the integration occurs. Also, in multiple integrals, one integral sign is often made to serve for all the differentials which follow it if there is no question of the limits of integration.

This is called **reducing the distribution function.** Clearly, *all* reduced distribution functions may be obtained from the *complete* distribution function by integrating over the appropriate variables.

Just as in Eq. 4-21, a higher order distribution function will factor if it expresses the dependence of the probability on uncorrelated parameters. Since the probability $f_{ij}(x_i, x_j)\, dx_i\, dx_j$ must factor, f_{ij} must factor, and

$$f_{ij}(x_i, x_j) = f_i(x_i) f_j(x_j) \tag{4-29}$$

if i and j are uncorrelated.

PROBLEMS

4-1. Consider the situation of Eq. 4-5, in which characteristics i and j are *not* mutually exclusive. Express the probability $P(i \text{ or } j)$ of finding *at least* characteristic i or characteristic j in terms of $P(i)$, $P(j)$, and the joint probability $P(i \text{ and } j)$.

4-2. Prove that Eq. 4-20 follows from Eq. 4-19.

4-3. If i and j are two characteristics of interest, the **conditional probability** of i under the condition j, $P(i \mid j)$, is defined by

$$P(i \mid j) = \frac{n(i \text{ and } j)}{n(j)}.$$

Note that the condition j means that all members of the ensemble that play any role must have j. Then the fraction of those that also have i is $P(i \mid j)$. If i and j are uncorrelated, express that fact in terms of $P(i \mid j)$ and discuss the result.

4-4. Conditional probabilities are defined in Prob. 4-3. The usual probabilities based on the complete ensemble are called **absolute probabilities.** Examples are $P_i(l_i)$ and $P_j(l_j)$. Express the joint probability $P_{ij}(l_i, l_j)$ in the general case *in two different ways* as the product of an absolute probability and a conditional probability.

4-5. If $h(l_1, l_2, \ldots, l_s)$ is any function of the s parameters that characterize a member of the ensemble, derive the expression for the ensemble average of h— first, when the parameters are discrete, in terms of the complete probability; second, when the parameters are continuous, in terms of the complete distribution function.

4-6. Express $f_{3,4}(l_3, l_4)$ in terms of $f_{1,2,\ldots,6}(l_1, l_2, \ldots, l_6)$. Express $f_{1,3,6}$ in terms of $f_{1,2,\ldots,6}$. Express the ensemble average of $h(l_2, l_3, l_5)$ in terms of an integral over $f_{1,2,\ldots,6}$. Express this same average as an integral over $f_{2,3,5}(l_2, l_3, l_5)$.

4-7. In the paragraph following Eq. 4-16, it is stated that $P_{ij}(l_i, l_j)$ contains more information than $P_i(l_i)$ and $P_j(l_j)$ do between them. Precisely what is the additional information? Is there any circumstance under which knowing P_i and P_j separately would furnish as much information as knowing P_{ij}?

5 THE ENSEMBLE IN STATISTICAL MECHANICS

This section treats the way that statistical mechanics uses probability theory. In particular, it determines what the members of the ensemble are like, what their characteristics are, and what parameters represent these characteristics. Not until Secs. 6 to 8 will consideration be given to finding what function of the parameters the probabilities are.

The problem of statistical mechanics begins with a physical system about which some macroscopic information is known. The system is considered to be a mechanical object made up of its constituent particles. The known macroscopic information is far short of a complete mechanical specification of the state of the N particles. Yet, mechanics is useful only when applied to particles in a completely specified mechanical state. Imagine how useful classical mechanics would be, for example, in discussing a game of billiards if one knew only that the three balls were "someplace on the billiard table."

It is this very lack of detailed information that requires the addition of probability theory to the mechanics. Since we do not *know* what mechanical state the N particles are in, we say that each possible state has its own probability. This probability distribution for the various states is a function of the information that is known about the system. It is hoped that the probabilities used will lead to conclusions which actually correspond to the probabilities of various results of measurements on the system.

Another way to express this is to say: *One constructs an ensemble to represent the system. Each member of the ensemble is a mental creation which is in a definite mechanical state. However, all members of the ensemble must reflect the known macroscopic information about the system.* Since that much is known about the system, the probability of its not having those known properties is zero. Thus, all the members of the ensemble must reflect that information.

A clear distinction must be drawn between the system and a member of the ensemble. The system is the physical object about which we hope to make predictions. Members of the ensemble are only mental constructions which give substance to the use of probability theory. Of course, we do not need to construct, even mentally, an infinite number of members with 10^{23} particles in a fixed mechanical state.* We only seek the complete probability as a mathematical function of the necessary parameters. The ensemble and its members are nevertheless useful to think about; they give a tangible feeling to the various probabilities, which might otherwise seem very abstract functions.

Choice of suitable parameters to characterize the members of the ensemble depends on the definition of a completely specified mechanical state for the N particles. In turn, this depends on the kind of mechanics being employed in determining the microscopic picture: quantum,† classical, or a mixture of both, which has acquired the name "semiclassical mechanics."

CLASSICAL MECHANICS‡

In classical mechanics, an N-particle state is completely specified when the position and momentum of each particle are given. If the particles are polyatomic molecules, the position and momentum of each atom must be given. If the system is considered to be composed of N classical mechanical particles, the complete set of parameters that characterizes a member of the ensemble is the set of N position vectors that locates the particles and the set of N momentum vectors, one for each particle. Since a vector is given by three numbers, say, its x, y, and z components, there are $6N$ continuous parameters characterizing each member of a classical ensemble.

The word "momentum" has been used here, rather than "velocity," despite the fact that momenta and velocities are often simply related. The reason is that classical statistical mechanics is much simpler when the variables used are the positions of the particles and the momenta appropriate to these positions. Throughout physics, momenta appear as more fundamental mechanical variables than velocities.

The $3N$ position components plus the $3N$ appropriate momentum

---

* Statistical mechanics credits people with great hypothetical mental agility. Still, it makes only reasonable demands.

† Actually, this book never considers a consistent quantum mechanical treatment, which would be based on the density matrix. This is discussed by Tolman, Chap. IX. If required, its study should prove much simpler after reading this book.

‡ Most of the larger references given in Appendix A, which cover either quantum mechanics or statistical mechanics, have chapters devoted to classical mechanics. The most thorough presentation is probably that of Tolman, Chaps. II and III, but it is difficult.

components which together form the complete set of parameters for the classical ensemble have been given the name of the **phase space** of the classical problem. Just as a point in ordinary space is the specification of the three coordinates that locate it, a point in phase space is the specification of the $6N$ coordinates that locate it. Thus, ordinary Cartesian space is three-dimensional and phase space is $6N$-dimensional. Each member of the classical ensemble is completely characterized by a single point in phase space. Sometimes the $3N$ position components are referred to separately as the **configuration space** of the problem and the $3N$ momentum components as the **momentum space.** This makes the complete phase space the sum of configuration space plus momentum space.

The concept of phase space is discussed in greater detail in Sec. 13, where the classical picture is actually used.

QUANTUM MECHANICS*

In quantum mechanics, a system whose volume is finite may exist in any one of an enormous number of *discrete* states. Since the allowed quantum states are discrete, they can in theory be ordered in some arbitrary way and a number given to each state. This single quantum number will completely specify the quantum state for the N particles. Therefore, the only parameter needed to describe a member of the ensemble in the quantum mechanical picture is this single discrete number.

The mechanical behavior of particles in nature is in fact described by quantum mechanics, not classical. One might ask why classical mechanics with its $6N$ different continuous parameters is ever used in statistical mechanics. The reasons are several. Quantum mechanics with its single discrete parameter is simple in principle, but the job of finding what the allowed quantum states are for an N-particle system is usually impossibly difficult. In classical mechanics, that part of the problem at least is solved. Also, classical mechanics has the advantage that it is easier to visualize N particles, each with its three position coordinates and three momentum coordinates, than it is an N-particle quantum state. Sometimes the quantum and classical pictures become identical, and these cases help one learn how to choose whichever description is needed to simplify the problem at hand.

---

* There are many satisfactory books on quantum mechanics, some of which are listed in Appendix A. Also, most of the larger books listed there that deal with statistical mechanics have chapters devoted to quantum mechanics as well.

SEMI-CLASSICAL MECHANICS

One last description of the microscopic picture is often useful. In many cases, the positions and momenta of the particles may very adequately be described by classical mechanics. However, the particles themselves may have complicated structure (such as polyatomic mole-. cules). The internal state of a molecule may almost never be described adequately by classical mechanics. A quantum description is necessary. What is done in this case is to describe the centers of mass of the molecules by classical positions and momenta and to use quantum mechanics to describe the internal states of the molecules. Such a mixed or hybrid description has commonly been called *semi-classical*.

The parameters needed to describe a member of a semi-classical ensemble are the following: $3N$ continuous position components for the centers of mass of the N particles, $3N$ continuous momentum components for the centers of mass of the N particles, and the set of discrete quantum numbers needed to fix the internal state of each of the N particles. If v different quantum numbers describe the internal state of each particle, then a member of a semi-classical ensemble is characterized completely by $(6 + v)N$ parameters.

The purely classical description is adequate only when one has no interest in the internal states of the molecules. Such a case could be the study of a monatomic fluid like an inert gas. If the atoms all are in their lowest electronic state, the fact that the atoms actually have a structure of their own may be neglected. As the temperature is increased and electronic excitation becomes more probable, the structure begins to play an active role in the physical properties. Then, even gases like argon must be treated semi-classically. In Parts II and III, all three descriptions will have occasion to be used.

DISCUSSION

Just how valid is the statistical mechanical approach? It is likely that it represents the ultimate in "scientific truth." All measurements on systems yield partial information. If one were able to look at a system and learn the exact position, momentum, and internal state of each particle, then the ensemble would have to reflect that information. Each member of the ensemble would then have to be identical. An ensemble consisting of just one member would be adequate, and that member would be identical to the system. In that case it would be meaningless to introduce the concept of probability into the many-particle mechanics used to study the system. There would be no need for *statistical* mechanics.

However, complete information is never obtained; yet with the partial information obtainable, one still wishes to predict as accurately as possible the results of measurements. Statistical mechanics can give this prediction and give it correctly—it consists in the distribution of probabilities of various measurements on a system, which is, naturally, a function of the information previously known about the system.

In the long run, as with any theory, the success of statistical mechanics rests on its usefulness in practice. It has proved very useful in the instances where its mathematical difficulties have not been excessive. Its usefulness in the future in more difficult cases will depend on whether it can be visualized more and more simply, thus easing the mathematical difficulties. The rapid development of large computers will certainly help. Recent work by Alder and Wainwright,* points to an interesting direction of investigation by actually following the mechanical motion of a large number of classical particles on a computer.

6 THE ISOLATED EQUILIBRIUM SYSTEM

This section treats the method whereby the macroscopic information known about the system is incorporated into the ensemble. At this point it is necessary to particularize to only those systems known to be "in equilibrium." This eliminates many fascinating and useful topics from consideration, but treating non-equilibrium problems would quadruple the length of this book and leave the reader far from satisfied at the end. Non-equilibrium statistical mechanics is a current research field, one which has been fought over for about a century. It has a way to go yet.

In Sec. 5, three different commonly employed microscopic pictures

* B. J. Alder and T. E. Wainwright, *J. Chem. Phys.*, **27**, 1208 (1957); **31**, 459 (1959); **33**, 1439 (1960).

were discussed, along with the parameters used in each picture to characterize a member of the ensemble. The rest of Part I is based on a purely quantum description. Not only are the formal manipulations simpler, but also, after all, quantum mechanics is the correct description of a system of particles. In Parts II and III, methods of passing to the classical and semi-classical pictures when appropriate will be examined in detail.

THE EQUILIBRIUM CONDITION

Systems known to be "in equilibrium" may be in one of several conditions. The three most commonly encountered are the following:

1. The system is a volume V containing N particles of known type *completely isolated* by insulating walls from the rest of the universe.

2. The system is a volume V containing N particles of known type *in thermal contact* with a heat reservoir or thermometer which is characterized by the temperature T.

3. The system is a volume V *in thermal contact* with a heat reservoir or thermometer which is characterized by the temperature T, and it is also *open to the exchange of matter* with a particle bath or reservoir which is characterized by the chemical potential μ.

In this section, condition 1 is studied; the resulting ensemble is called *microcanonical*. In Sec. 7, condition 2 is studied; the resulting ensemble is called *canonical*. In Sec. 33, condition 3 is studied; the resulting ensemble is called *grand canonical*.

In all cases, the system is known to be "at equilibrium." It is therefore necessary to define the equilibrium condition carefully. One associates time independence with equilibrium and also a certain constancy in macroscopic properties. However, as one examines any macroscopic "equilibrium" system more and more closely, he learns much specific information about it. Local variables, such as the density, will be found to fluctuate from place to place in the system. These fluctuations, caused by the motion of the particles in the system, are constantly arising and being dissipated. So if one knows too much about a system that would otherwise be considered "in equilibrium," he destroys the time independence associated with the equilibrium condition.

The ensemble which correctly represents the equilibrium condition must simultaneously represent all possible fluctuations, each weighted according to its probability. Constancy in macroscopic properties is not *required* of a system known to be "in equilibrium." The extent to which constancy is expected should be calculable from the probability function, however. Time independence, on the other hand, is certainly part of the equilibrium condition. The time independence rests not in the macroscopic properties of the physical system, but in the state of knowledge one has about the system. With condition 1 above, he knows that the volume is is constant, the number and type of particles are constant, and the energy of the system is constant. Furthermore, his own state of ignorance about any other features of the system is constant. The system may have got into its equilibrium condition from any of a number of previous conditions, but it has sat around long enough that it now is "at equilibrium." Information about its former condition is completely lost.

In statistical mechanics, *a system is in a condition of* **equilibrium** *when the information one has about it has reached a time independent minimum.* This condition depends only on the material comprising the system and its constraints (such as fixed volume, energy, temperature). It is independent of the system's history. In order to rule out so-called "steady states," one should also require that the immediate surroundings of the equilibrium system be in equilibrium too.

THE MICROCANONICAL ENSEMBLE

Consider an equilibrium system in condition 1 above. Knowledge of the type and number of particles and of the system volume is sufficient for quantum mechanics in principle to determine all the many allowed N-particle quantum states.* The states can all be ordered, perhaps in order of increasing energy, and a number assigned to each.

The only additional knowledge possessed is that the system is isolated and therefore has a fixed energy E_{system}. It is desired to build this information, and this information only, into the ensemble. There must be no spurious information built into the ensemble accidentally. One faces this enormous number of allowed quantum states, each of which must be assigned a probability. The only dynamical feature known about the system is its energy E_{system}. Therefore, he places the following requirement on the complete probability at equilibrium: *The only dynamical feature on which the probability of a state may depend is the energy of the state.* The probability of the ith N-particle quantum state may be denoted by $P_N(i)$. Thus, $P_N(i)$ is the fraction of the members of the ensemble that

* If the classical or semi-classical picture were being used, this knowledge would still determine all the allowed mechanical states, and thus all the parameters needed to describe a member of the ensemble.

are in quantum state i. The above requirement may then be written

$$P_N(i) = P_N(E_i), \tag{6-1}$$

where E_i is the energy of the N particles in quantum state i.

This requirement or hypothesis bears some discussion, since on it is based all of equilibrium statistical mechanics. Suppose the probabilities of the allowed quantum states were assigned as functions of something other than the energy—for example, the number of particles in a particular cubic centimeter of the system. That would mean that for some reason we were biasing the probability distribution for or against certain numbers of particles in that cubic centimeter.* However, without having measured the number of particles there, we have no right to bias the distribution in that way. And if we had made the measurement, we would have too much information for an "equilibrium" system and the time independence would be destroyed, as discussed above.

Thus, the basic hypothesis of Eq. 6-1 seems to have been forced on us. Anything other than the energy on which the probabilities might be allowed to depend would not have been part of the macroscopic information available under these circumstances. Such additional information would have been spurious, thus having no place in the ensemble. Nevertheless, Eq. 6-1 may be viewed as an assumption if one wishes, or else as a consequence of the aims of statistical mechanics.

An interesting consequence of Eq. 6-1 is the fact that *all quantum states with the same energy have the same probability.* In quantum mechanics, two different states are called **degenerate** if they represent systems with the same energy. Since $P_N(i)$ is a function only of the value of E_i, the probabilities of all degenerate quantum states are equal.

> One might ask whether an ensemble constructed in some way according to Eq. 6-1 would remain independent of time as each member evolved. The answer is that it would, and the proof is based on a rather general conclusion from quantum mechanics called the *principle of detailed balancing.*† This principle says that the probability that a member of the ensemble in state A will go into state B is the same as that of one in state B going into state A. The transition is only allowed at all if energy is conserved, so the energy of A and B are equal. Therefore, at equilibrium the ensemble has the same number of members in both A and B. Since on the average the same number per unit time go from A to B as go from B to A, the structure of the ensemble remains constant in time.

---

* This type of biasing is treated mathematically in the discipline called "information theory." In the opinion of the author, the mathematics of information theory is less convincing than the simple physics of the problem. The interested reader may consult L. Brillouin, *Science and Information Theory*, Academic Press, New York, 2d edition, 1962.

† Tolman, p. 521; Powell and Crasemann, p. 420.

The system being considered in this section has measured energy, and, since it is isolated from the rest of the universe, it must keep that energy.* Each member of the ensemble must have this same energy, E_{system}. Thus, $P_N(i)$ is identically zero for states whose energy differs from E_{system}, and $P_N(i)$ is $P_N(E_{\text{system}})$ for the others:

$$P_N(i) = \begin{cases} P_N(E_{\text{system}}) & (E_i = E_{\text{system}}), \\ 0 & (E_i \neq E_{\text{system}}) \end{cases}. \tag{6-2}$$

Only the degenerate states with energy E_{system} have non-vanishing probabilities, the same constant value for all such states.

A distribution of probabilities constructed according to Eq. 6-2 to represent an equilibrium system of fixed energy is what Gibbs called a *microcanonical distribution*. The ensemble that such a distribution represents is called a *microcanonical ensemble*. Gibbs did not say why he chose this name, but the name has stuck. The "micro" prefix connotes the *micro*scopically sharp energy requirement. The "canonical" connotes the *general acceptance* of the ensemble described by Eq. 6-2 as representative of the isolated equilibrium system.

The microcanonical distribution of probabilities of N-particle quantum states, as given in Eq. 6-2, is a reflection of the following necessary and sufficient conditions:

1. The probability of an N-particle quantum state is a function only of the energy of that state.

2. The system has known total energy E_{system}.

PROBLEM

6-1. Suppose there are $\mathcal{N}$ quantum states for an N-particle system which have total energy E_{system}. What is the value of $P_N(i)$ for a particular quantum state?

---

* Or very close to it. Actually, there is always an uncertainty in the energy of any system due to the Heisenberg principle. Broadening slightly the sharp energy requirement of this section changes the conclusions in no important way.

7 SYSTEM IN EQUILIBRIUM WITH A HEAT BATH

Suppose that instead of being isolated, the equilibrium system of interest is known to be at a certain temperature because it is "in equilibrium with a heat bath characterized by that temperature." This is the second possible equilibrium condition discussed at the beginning of Sec. 6. This section considers the question of what is implied in the use of the following distribution of probabilities for this isothermal case:

$$P_N(i) = ae^{-\beta E_i}. \tag{7-1}$$

Gibbs called the distribution represented by Eq. 7-1 the **canonical distribution,** and ensembles constructed in this way **canonical ensembles.**

An interpretation of Eq. 7-1 rests on the realization that the energy of each N-particle quantum state is usually capable of being written as the sum of small energy contributions: kinetic energies of the individual particles, potential energies of the particles relative to external fields, internal energies of the various molecules, intermolecular potential energies, and perhaps others. This fact may be written

$$E_i = \epsilon_1 + \epsilon_2 + \epsilon_3 + \cdots, \tag{7-2}$$

where the ϵ's are the many small contributions.

MATHEMATICAL IMPLICATIONS

To prove: A necessary condition for the use of Eq. 7-1 is that the only dynamical feature on which the probability of a state may depend be the energy of the state. (This condition is the same as that given by Eq. 6-1.)

Proof: Simple examination of Eq. 7-1 shows the statement to be true. The quantity a is determined by normalization, and the quantity β is shown in Sec. 9 to be $1/kT$, where T is the absolute temperature and k is a constant. The only thing left in Eq. 7-1 is E_i. Q.E.D.

To prove: A necessary condition for the use of Eq. 7-1 is that $P_N(E_i)$ *factor,* with a separate term for each contribution of Eq. 7-2.

Proof: Inserting Eq. 7-2 into Eq. 7-1 yields

$$P_N(i) = ae^{-\beta\epsilon_1} \cdot e^{-\beta\epsilon_2} \cdot e^{-\beta\epsilon_3} \cdots . \qquad \text{Q.E.D.} \qquad (7\text{-}3)$$

To prove: The two necessary conditions just given are also sufficient conditions for the use of Eq. 7-1. In other words, the two necessary conditions are enough to *force* the canonical form, Eq. 7-1.

Proof: The first necessary condition is Eq. 6-1:

$$P_N(i) = P_N(E) = P_N(\epsilon_1 + \epsilon_2 + \cdots). \qquad (7\text{-}4)$$

The second condition is that P_N factor. Coupled with Eq. 7-4, this becomes

$$P_N(\epsilon_1 + \epsilon_2 + \cdots) = P_1(\epsilon_1) \cdot P_2(\epsilon_2) \cdots , \qquad (7\text{-}5)$$

$$\ln P_N(\epsilon_1 + \epsilon_2 + \cdots) = \ln P_1(\epsilon_1) + \ln P_2(\epsilon_2) + \cdots . \qquad (7\text{-}6)$$

Equation 7-6 is simply the logarithm of Eq. 7-5. If Eq. 7-6 is differentiated with respect to ϵ_j, it becomes

$$\frac{\partial \ln P_N(E)}{\partial \epsilon_j} = \frac{\partial \ln P_j(\epsilon_j)}{\partial \epsilon_j} \qquad (7\text{-}7)$$

$$\frac{\partial \ln P_N(E)}{\partial E} \frac{dE}{d\epsilon_j} = \frac{\partial \ln P_j(\epsilon_j)}{\partial \epsilon_j} , \qquad (7\text{-}8)$$

$$\frac{\partial \ln P_N(E)}{\partial E} = \frac{\partial \ln P_j(\epsilon_j)}{\partial \epsilon_j} . \qquad (7\text{-}9)$$

Since the left-hand side of Eq. 7-9 is in no way a peculiar function of ϵ_j but is just a function of E, it clearly made no difference in Eq. 7-7 which ϵ was chosen for the differentiation. The result would be the same. Thus the right-hand side of Eq. 7-9, which at most could be a function of ϵ_j, must not even depend on ϵ_j and must be a constant. The result is simply

$$\frac{\partial \ln P_N}{\partial E} = \frac{\partial \ln P_j}{\partial \epsilon_j} = \text{constant}. \qquad (7\text{-}10)$$

If the left and right sides of Eq. 7-10 are multiplied by dE and integrated, we obtain

$$\ln P_N = -\beta E + A, \qquad (7\text{-}11)$$

where the constant of Eq. 7-10 is called $-\beta$. The integration constant A of Eq. 7-11 may be called $\ln a$ and Eq. 7-11 may be rewritten

$$P_N(E) = ae^{-\beta E}. \qquad \text{Q.E.D.} \qquad (7\text{-}12)$$

PHYSICAL IMPLICATIONS

The implications of the first condition for the validity of the canonical ensemble, Eq. 7-4, are discussed in Sec. 6. The only other condition is that $P_N(E)$ must factor, with a separate term giving a separate independent probability for each contribution in the sum, Eq. 7-2.

This condition is seen to be met as soon as one has a picture of the mechanical purpose of the heat bath. In Eq. 7-1 it is clear that states with *any* value of E_i have finite probabilities. There is no restriction whatever on the size of E_i, as there is in the microcanonical ensemble. This is because one does not know the energy of the system. The system might indeed have any energy. All that is known is that the system is in equilibrium with a heat bath. This bath must be capable of giving up or receiving any finite amount of energy without appreciably changing. Therefore, one pictures the heat bath as an infinitely large* system at equilibrium.

The last remaining question is why such a heat bath permits P_N to be factored, as in Eq. 7-5. First we must ask what is present in the system to correlate explicitly the contributions in the various ϵ's, and thus prevent this factorization. For example, what physical feature might correlate the amount of kinetic energy of some particle with the amount of rotational energy of another particle way off in another part of the system? In fact, it is interesting that whatever this physical feature is, it must correlate *all* the ϵ's with each other and in exactly the same way, however they are defined. This is a consequence of the fact that P_N is a function only of the sum of the various ϵ's. Any function of the sum must be completely symmetric in the terms in the sum.

Clearly, the only correlation of this type imaginable would be *some requirement on the total energy of the system*. For example, if the system were isolated, its energy would be fixed. Thus, all the ϵ's would have to add to give E_{system}. In that case, if one of the ϵ's were an appreciable fraction of the total energy available, this would be felt as a limitation on the energy available to all the other contributions. The presence of the heat bath eliminates this type of correlation. There being no other physical feature that could correlate the ϵ's explicitly, P_N must factor, and the canonical form follows.

* Actually, it makes little difference for macroscopic systems how large the heat bath is or even whether there is one. Due to the enormous number of particles contained in macroscopic systems, the probability that the system energy departs appreciably from its average value is negligible, even if an infinite heat bath were present. This makes the canonical ensemble useful for calculations even when the heat bath is either small or non-existent. This is proved and discussed in Sec. 33. However, *rigorous* use of Eq. 7-1 clearly demands an infinite heat bath.

The canonical distribution differs from the microcanonical in that the requirement of microscopically sharp total energy is removed. The system may have any energy. However, all N-particle quantum states with the same energy have the same probability. We might think of a canonical ensemble as constructed from a large number of microcanonical ensembles, one for each different possible value of E, weighted according to Eq. 7-1.

Both the microcanonical and the canonical ensembles represent a system with a fixed number of particles N. Gibbs called these *petit ensembles,* in contrast with those in which the number of particles N is not fixed. The latter he called **grand ensembles,** and they may be considered as composed of a large number of petit ensembles, weighted to give the desired dependence of the probability on the number of particles. Grand ensembles are considered in Sec. 33.

In concluding the discussion of the canonical distribution, it must be emphasized that the exponential form, Eq. 7-1, still may represent correlations between parts of the system; not explicit, but implicit. For example, consider two particles. Of the group of ϵ's, one may be chosen to represent the potential energy of interaction between these particles. When they are close together, this is large and affects markedly the probability of the configuration. When they are far apart, this is small and may be neglected. Clearly the two particles are correlated, in that probabilities involving one of them depend on the position of the other through terms in the energy involving both their positions simultaneously. This type of correlation is discussed further in Secs. 26 to 28.

In summary, the canonical distribution of probabilities of N-particle quantum states, as given in Eq. 7-1, is a reflection of the following necessary and sufficient conditions:

1. The probability of an N-particle quantum state is a function only of the energy of that state. Note: It must be meaningful to talk about separate quantum states for the system. If the system is interacting too strongly with its surroundings for this to be so, then the theory breaks down.

2. The system is only an infinitesimal part of a composite equilibrium situation consisting of system plus heat bath. The only purpose of the heat bath is to serve as an infinite source or sink of energy.

PROBLEM

7-1. At the beginning of Sec. 6, there is a list of the information initially known about three different commonly encountered equilibrium conditions. Equations 6-2 and 7-1 give the probability distributions that represent the first two of these. Discuss for each of these two how each bit of initial information enters the probability distribution. Is there any information in the probability distribution that was not initially known?

8   EXPONENTIAL REDUCED PROBABILITIES

In many cases, the probabilities for quantum states of the complete N-particle system are not necessary. We are sometimes interested only in how much of the total energy is present in one or two of the contributions ϵ that make up E. This section considers partially the question of when the reduced probability for a few energy contributions can legitimately be expressed as

$$\boxed{P_j(\epsilon_j) = \alpha e^{-\beta \epsilon_j}.}$$ (8-1)

Equation 8-1 is the well-known **Boltzmann distribution** of energies, and $e^{-\beta \epsilon_j}$ by itself is often called the **Boltzmann factor.**

The desire to look at just a few of the ϵ's necessitates a change in the parameters used to describe the ensemble. Instead of simply listing the quantum state i, we may give the values of all the ϵ's.* Then $P_N(E_i)$ may be thought of as the *joint probability* that the first contribution is ϵ_1 *and* the second is ϵ_2 *and* the third is ϵ_3 *and* . . . . Since there may well be more than 10^{23} ϵ's in the sum, Eq. 7-1, our interest is in the very much reduced probability describing the expected distribution of energy in just a few of these parts of the system. One condition that must certainly be met is that it be meaningful to view state i as this joint probability, with physical meaning attached to each ϵ. For a system composed of identical particles, this condition is not trivial. It is discussed in Sec. 22.

---

* Often a mere listing of the ϵ's does not uniquely determine the quantum state for the system. Several different quantum states may have the same set of ϵ's. This introduces nothing new to the analysis of this section, since a slight complication of the notation permits the formulation of Eq. 8-1 in complete analogy to the way we have formulated it here. It must be emphasized that Eq. 8-1 gives the probability that a small part j of the system is in a particular quantum state which has energy ϵ_j. If several states for part j have the same energy, each has the same probability, Eq. 8-1.

For the moment, suppose the system to be represented by a canonical ensemble,

$$P_N(i) = ae^{-\beta E_i} = ae^{-\beta(\epsilon_1 + \epsilon_2 + \cdots)}. \tag{8-2}$$

This complete probability may be reduced to $P_j(\epsilon_j)$ by summing over all allowed values of all the ϵ's except ϵ_j. This is analogous to Eq. 4-18:

$$P_j(\epsilon_j) = a \sum_{\epsilon_1, \epsilon_2, \ldots \text{except } \epsilon_j} \cdots \sum e^{-\beta(\epsilon_1 + \epsilon_2 + \cdots)}. \tag{8-3}$$

In order for Eq. 8-3 to simplify to Eq. 8-1, a second condition is necessary: The sets of values of ϵ's over which the summations are performed must be independent of the value of ϵ_j. This condition is generally not met in physical systems, but in many cases it may be approximated. The problem is discussed in Sec. 17. When the approximation of independence is made, the multiple sum just gives a constant A which may be combined with a to yield the new constant α:

$$P_j(\epsilon_j) = ae^{-\beta\epsilon_j} \sum_{\epsilon_1, \epsilon_2, \ldots \text{except } \epsilon_j} \cdots \sum e^{-\beta(E-\epsilon_j)} \tag{8-4}$$

$$= ae^{-\beta\epsilon_j} \cdot A, \tag{8-5}$$

$$P_j(\epsilon_j) = \alpha e^{-\beta\epsilon_j}. \tag{8-6}$$

With this result, the Boltzmann distribution, we can say that the particles "obey Boltzmann statistics."

The last question we have on the validity of the Boltzmann distribution is whether one must start with a canonical ensemble for the system. Must the system be in equilibrium with a heat bath before the Boltzmann distribution is valid? This question can be easily answered (in the negative) if we refer back to the purpose of the heat bath, as discussed in Sec. 7. It was seen there to be simply a source or sink of energy which permits any value of the total energy to be possible. Suppose the system is isolated; then the microcanonical distribution properly describes it, and there is the restriction

$$\epsilon_1 + \epsilon_2 + \cdots = E_{\text{system}}. \tag{8-7}$$

For $P_j(\epsilon_j)$ to differ from Eq. 8-1, however, the physical processes that lead to part j getting its share of the energy must explicitly feel the requirement of Eq. 8-7. If part j is only an infinitesimal portion of the total system, the interesting values of its energy will be infinitesimal fractions of E_{system}. We would not expect part j's energy to be influenced by Eq. 8-7 under such circumstances. All the other parts of the system, with which part j is interacting, may be viewed as an effective "heat bath." This permits the reduced distribution function to be exponential, even though the system as a whole is isolated. We may incorporate this physical conclusion into the theory by using the Boltzmann distribution for infinitesimal parts of even isolated systems, so long as the other conditions for the validity of Eq. 8-1 are met.

With an isolated system, very large values of ϵ would be even less probable than as given by Eq. 8-1 because of the effect of the restriction Eq. 8-7 in eliminating N-particle states from consideration. In fact, ϵ's greater than E_{system} must have zero probability, rather than the exponential. However, for systems containing an enormous number of particles, $e^{-\beta\epsilon}$ is already so small by the time ϵ becomes comparable to E_{system} that the difference between the exact probability and the exponential is completely negligible.

In summary, the Boltzmann distribution of reduced probabilities for a portion of the system, as given in Eq. 8-1, is a reflection of the following necessary and sufficient conditions:

1. The probability of an N-particle quantum state is a function only of the energy of that state.

2. The part j of the system whose energy is being considered has physical significance.

3. The amount of energy ϵ_j present in part j is only an infinitesimal fraction of the total energy available to the N particles.

4. The sets of values of energies the other parts of the system may have are for all practical purposes independent of the value of ϵ_j.

Consider a system for which the Boltzmann distribution is valid. This being so, the ratio of the probability of finding a given particle in state i to that of finding it in state j is

$$\frac{P(\epsilon_i)}{P(\epsilon_j)} = e^{-\beta(\epsilon_i - \epsilon_j)}. \tag{8-8}$$

In a very loose usage of language, Eq. 8-8 is commonly said to give the ratio of the *populations* of the two states. This usage is discussed further in Sec. 22. Clearly, it is most unlikely for particles to be in states i which have $\epsilon_i - \epsilon_j \gg 1/\beta$. The "natural" unit or measure of energy is β^{-1}. Since β is shown in Sec. 9 to be $1/kT$, another way to say this is that the "natural" unit of temperature is $1/kT$.

Sometimes several distinct particle states have the same energy. Such an energy level is called *degenerate*. Its *degeneracy is equal to the number of different particle states with that energy.* Suppose level i had a degeneracy g_i and level j a degeneracy g_j. Then the ratio of the probability of finding a given particle in a state with energy ϵ_i to that of finding it in a state with energy ϵ_j is

$$\frac{\sum\limits_{i=1}^{g_i} P(\epsilon_i)}{\sum\limits_{j=1}^{g_j} P(\epsilon_j)} = \frac{g_i P(\epsilon_i)}{g_j P(\epsilon_j)} = \frac{g_i}{g_j} e^{-\beta(\epsilon_i - \epsilon_j)}. \tag{8-9}$$

It is important to realize the difference between what is expressed by Eq. 8-8 and what is expressed by Eq. 8-9. The introduction of the degeneracies g, often called the **statistical weights,** redirects one's concern from quantum states to energy levels. The energy level language is not used in this book, although it is in many. Changing from one language to the other is easy, however, because the number of states contributing to a degenerate level is simply the degeneracy of the level.

PROBLEMS

8-1. Discuss in your own words the reason why reduced probabilities for isolated equilibrium systems may be considered as exponentials of the energy.

8-2. Discuss the difference between the following two mathematical expressions:

$$\exp\left(-\sum_i \epsilon_i/kT\right) \text{ and } \sum_i \exp\left(-\epsilon_i/kT\right).$$

9   ENERGY AND ENTROPY IN STATISTICAL MECHANICS

In this section the statistical mechanical analogs of the energy and entropy of thermodynamics are found, giving a mechanical interpretation to all of thermodynamics. The presentation is limited to systems represented by a canonical ensemble, and the thermodynamic variables are found as averages over this ensemble. These would be the logical values to predict for a system in equilibrium with a heat bath. As noted in Sec. 3, the ensemble average may not always agree with what is found in a system. The problem of how near the ensemble average the thermodynamic variables are expected to lie is treated in Sec. 33. Also, the use of canonical ensembles to represent even isolated systems is discussed there. These problems need cause no concern until then.

The probability of the ith N-particle quantum state is

$$P_N(i) = ae^{-\beta E_i}, \tag{9-1}$$

where a is the normalizing constant:

$$\sum_i P_N(i) = 1 = a \sum_i e^{-\beta E_i},$$

$$a = \frac{1}{\sum_i e^{-\beta E_i}} . \tag{9-2}$$

The reciprocal of the normalizing constant is given the symbol Q (in some books, Z) and is simply the sum over all states of the exponential:

$$\boxed{Q = \frac{1}{a} = \sum_i e^{-\beta E_i}.} \tag{9-3}$$

The sum Q has a central role in statistical thermodynamics, because once it is known as a function of the variables on which it depends, all thermodynamic quantities may be calculated from it directly. Planck called it the *Zustandssumme*, and for a while (Tolman) there was hope that the natural translation, *sum-over-states*, would become its English name. However, the name **partition function,** used by Darwin and Fowler for an analogous quantity, has become generally accepted for Q.

Clearly, Q is a function only of β and of the set of available quantum states and their corresponding energies. The set of states in turn is found in principle by using quantum mechanics and is a function of only the number and nature of the particles comprising the system and the constraints. The only constraint on systems considered in this book is the volume; however, others could easily be incorporated. In summary, Q is a function of β, of V, and of the number and nature of particles.

In terms of the partition function, the probability of a state, Eq. 9-1, becomes

$$P_N(i) = \frac{e^{-\beta E_i}}{Q} . \tag{9-4}$$

In terms of Q, the ensemble average of the energy of an N-particle state is found in the manner of Eq. 4-9:

$$\bar{E} = \sum_i P_N(i)E_i = \frac{\sum_i e^{-\beta E_i} E_i}{Q}$$

$$= \frac{\sum_i E_i e^{-\beta E_i}}{\sum_i e^{-\beta E_i}} = -\frac{\partial \left(\ln \sum_i e^{-\beta E_i} \right)}{\partial \beta},$$

$$\boxed{\bar{E} = -\left(\frac{\partial \ln Q}{\partial \beta} \right)_{V,N}.} \tag{9-5}$$

The reader may immediately verify the convenient use of the derivative of the logarithm in representing the quotient.

In order to find the analog of the entropy, an expression must first be found for the reversible heat. Like Q itself, $\ln Q$ is a function only of β and V, if the number and type of particles are kept constant. If a *reversible* change is made in β and V, then the equilibrium probability, while changed, still is given by a canonical ensemble. The volume change alters the energy levels E_i:

$$d \ln Q = \left(\frac{\partial \ln Q}{\partial \beta} \right)_V d\beta + \sum_i \left(\frac{\partial \ln Q}{\partial E_i} \right)_\beta dE_i \tag{9-6}$$

$$= -\bar{E} \, d\beta - \beta \sum_i \frac{e^{-\beta E_i} \, dE_i}{Q}. \tag{9-7}$$

Recognition of $\partial \ln Q/\partial \beta$ was made using Eq. 9-5, and the last term is simply the result of differentiation. It clearly represents $-\beta \, \overline{dE}$, where $\overline{dE}$ is the ensemble average of the change in energy caused by the reversible change in volume. This is none other than the *work* done on the system. Thus, $\overline{dE}$ is the negative of the ensemble average of the reversible work done *by* the system. On noting now that

$$d(\bar{E}\beta) = \bar{E} \, d\beta + \beta \, d\bar{E}, \tag{9-8}$$

and using the symbol $\overline{\delta w}_{\text{rev}}$ for the negative of $\overline{dE}$, Eq. 9-7 becomes

$$d \ln Q = \beta \, d\bar{E} - d(\bar{E}\beta) + \beta \, \overline{\delta w}_{\text{rev}};$$

$$d(\ln Q + \bar{E}\beta) = \beta(d\bar{E} + \overline{\delta w}_{\text{rev}}). \tag{9-9}$$

Equation 9-9 arises from statistical mechanics. Thermodynamically, the heat is defined by the differential expression of the first law:

$$\delta q = dE + \delta w. \tag{9-10}$$

Use of this in Eq. 9-9 permits expressing the reversible heat in statistical mechanics:

$$d(\ln Q + \bar{E}\beta) = \beta \,\overline{\delta q_{\text{rev}}}. \tag{9-11}$$

One may view Eq. 9-11 as a statistical mechanical expression of part of the second law of thermodynamics—*the reversible heat possesses the integrating factor* 1/T, *which makes* δq_{rev}/T *the differential of a function of state, the entropy* S. The left-hand side of Eq. 9-11 is indeed the differential of a function of state (that is, a function which depends only on the number and kind of particles, the volume, and the temperature). Therefore, β must be proportional to $1/T$, where T is the *absolute thermodynamic temperature*. If the proportionality constant is called $1/k$, then

$$\boxed{\beta = \frac{1}{kT}.} \tag{9-12}$$

Choice of k essentially fixes the size of the unit of T. This is conventionally done by reference to the properties of the "ideal gas." In both Secs. 13 and 18 this reference is made and the value of k, called **Boltzmann's constant,** is determined.

The left-hand side of Eq. 9-11 may be identified as $1/k$ times the differential of the ensemble average of the entropy:

$$d\bar{S} = d\left(k \ln Q + \frac{\bar{E}}{T}\right). \tag{9-13}$$

If this is integrated from zero temperature to T, an expression is obtained for $\bar{S}$:

$$\bar{S} = k \ln Q + \frac{\bar{E}}{T} + \bar{S}_0. \tag{9-14}$$

The integration constant $\bar{S}_0$ does not depend either on the set of quantum states or on T. It is convenient to set $\bar{S}_0$ equal to zero. This practice is discussed in greater detail in Sec. 10. The entropy in statistical mechanics then becomes simply

$$\boxed{\bar{S} = k \ln Q + \frac{\bar{E}}{T}.} \tag{9-15}$$

In this section, the statistical mechanical expressions for the energy and entropy of a system have been obtained. Also, the parameter β of previous sections has been proved proportional to the reciprocal of the absolute temperature. The overbar has been used to indicate that $\bar{E}$ and $\bar{S}$ are ensemble averages of the energy and entropy. However, they must be the same as the E and S of classical thermodynamics. While the statistical mechanical picture permits fluctuations in the measured E and S of physical systems, the picture of classical thermodynamics does not allow this. Therefore, the unique values of E and S in thermodynamics must be the $\bar{E}$ and $\bar{S}$ of statistical mechanics. This question is discussed further in Secs. 33 and 34. The overbars could be dropped at this time, but they are retained for clarity. In the next section, the entropy is examined in greater detail and the third law of thermodynamics considered.

10   ENTROPY AND THE THIRD LAW

The entropy of a system as given by Eq. 9-14 is undetermined to within an additive constant $\bar{S}_0$. This constant is independent of both the temperature and the set of available N-particle quantum states. Therefore, if some final condition for the system could be reached by an imaginable reversible path from the initial condition of the system, then $\bar{S}_0$ would drop out in determining $\Delta \bar{S}$ for the process. The imaginable path must be reversible, since the results of Sec. 9 are valid only for reversible changes; the system must be represented by a canonical ensemble during the entire process under consideration. In calculating the entropy change $\Delta \bar{S}$ for any process for which a reversible path could be imagined, choice of $\bar{S}_0$ is immaterial. For simplicity, one sets $\bar{S}_0$ equal to zero. This is by no means necessary; the Helmholtz and Gibbs free energies could simply be redefined to eliminate $\bar{S}_0$. The physical content of these equations is unchanged by neglecting $\bar{S}_0$. This applies even to the third law of thermodynamics, discussed below.*

A more intuitive way of writing $\bar{S}$ may be obtained from Eq. 9-14 or 9-15 using the following identities:

$$\ln Q = -\ln a, \tag{10-1}$$

$$\sum_i P_N(i) = 1, \tag{10-2}$$

$$E_i = -kT \ln e^{-\beta E_i}. \tag{10-3}$$

* For an interesting discussion of the value of $\bar{S}_0$, see Schrödinger, pp. 15–17.

One finds, starting with Eq. 9-15,

$$\bar{S} = k \ln Q + \frac{\bar{E}}{T}$$

$$= -k \ln a + \frac{1}{T} \sum_i P_N(i) E_i$$

$$= -k \sum_i P_N(i) \ln a - k \sum_i P_N(i) \ln e^{-\beta E_i}$$

$$= -k \sum_i P_N(i) \ln (ae^{-\beta E_i}),$$

$$\boxed{\bar{S} = -k \sum_i P_N(i) \ln P_N(i),} \qquad (10\text{-}4)$$

$$\boxed{\bar{S} = -k \, \overline{\ln P_N}.} \qquad (10\text{-}5)$$

The entropy of the system is proportional to the ensemble average of the logarithm of the probability of an N-particle state. This average is a measure of how closely one can pinpoint the state he would expect the system to be in. A high degree of predictive ability regarding the system implies a low entropy and vice versa. The more quantum states available to a system, the higher the entropy. This is illustrated in the remainder of this section by some specific considerations.

Suppose the system is known for certain to be in a particular quantum state, state j. Then, in the summation of Eq. 10-4, $P_N(i)$ is zero for all states but j; $P_N(j)$ is unity, so $\ln P_N(j)$ is zero. Therefore, $\bar{S}$ is zero (or else $\bar{S}_0$) whenever the system is definitely known to be in a particular quantum state.

It might be possible under certain conditions to know the quantum state a system is in. At the absolute zero of temperature, the only states allowed non-vanishing probabilities by the canonical ensemble are those with the lowest lying energy. Each state with this lowest energy has the same probability $1/\mathcal{N}$, where $\mathcal{N}$ is the number of different N-particle states with the lowest energy (in other words, $\mathcal{N}$ is the degeneracy of the lowest energy level for the system). At absolute zero, the entropy is given by Eq. 10-4 as

$$\bar{S}(0°\text{K}) = -k \sum_{i=1}^{\mathcal{N}} \frac{1}{\mathcal{N}} \ln \frac{1}{\mathcal{N}}$$

$$= -k \ln \frac{1}{\mathcal{N}},$$

$$\boxed{\bar{S}(0°\text{K}) = k \ln \mathcal{N}.} \qquad (10\text{-}6)$$

Quantum mechanical calculations for some models of crystals show $\mathcal{N}$ to be unity, and thus $\bar{S}(0°\text{K})$ to be zero. A generalization of this, that $S \to 0$ as $T \to 0$, is known in thermodynamics as Planck's statement of the third law. In light of the discussion of $\bar{S}_0$ above, Planck's statement would be better replaced by the following: A *perfect crystal* is defined as one for which $\mathcal{N}$ is unity. Then, *the entropy change $\Delta \bar{S}$ is zero for any process at absolute zero for which a reversible path could be imagined, if the reactants and products are perfect crystals.* The mechanical formulation of the third law is seen as a consequence of Eq. 9-14.

The question is, are there any perfect crystals? The answer, probably not, but lots of them come close enough. A number of features involving the entire macroscopic crystal could lead to values of $\mathcal{N}$ other than unity. For example, crystals with permanent magnetic moments may be aligned in any one of several directions with the same energy. It is believed that, for most crystals completely in equilibrium at $0°K$, $\mathcal{N}$ is very small. However, for $\mathcal{N}$ even as large as in the millions or billions, $\bar{S}(0°K)$ for the crystal, as given by Eq. 10-6, is still of the order of k. In Part II, k is found to be about 3.3×10^{-24} cal/deg. Experiments measure entropies to at best 10^{-3} cal/deg. Clearly, $\mathcal{N}$ must be of the order of $10^{10^{20}}$ before the residual entropy of a crystal at absolute zero becomes measurable.

How might such an enormous value of $\mathcal{N}$ arise? The degeneracy must not be so much a property of the crystal as a whole as a property of the particles that make it up. In this way, advantage may be taken of the enormous size of N, the number of particles in the crystal.

As an example, consider crystalline carbon monoxide. While they are freezing out, the CO molecules have enough energy that it is immaterial to them in which direction they enter the lattice, CO or OC. After the crystal is formed and the temperature greatly reduced, the energy differences between a perfect and a random array may seem more important, but then it is too late for the CO molecules to turn around. They are frozen in. The resulting crystal with randomly oriented molecules may not have its lowest energy level quite so low as a more regular crystal, but the difference is not measurable. If an N-particle quantum state is specified by giving the direction of orientation of the CO molecule at each of the N lattice points in the crystal, then there are 2^N different quantum states available to the crystal of carbon monoxide at absolute zero. A number of this immensity leads to a measurable residual entropy:

$$\bar{S}(0°K) = k \ln 2^N = Nk \ln 2.$$

If N is Avogadro's number, this is 1.38 cal/mole-deg.

This has actually been observed,* as follows: The entropy of gaseous CO at room temperature was calculated by the methods of Part II of this

* J. O. Clayton and W. F. Giauque, *J. Am. Chem. Soc.*, **54**, 2610 (1932).

book. The result was compared with the entropy found by integrating the experimentally determined $\delta q_{rev}/T$ from almost $0°K$ up to room temperature. The experimental value proved to be less than the calculated by 1.0 cal/mole-deg. This suggests that $1.0N/1.38$ particles actually entered the crystal as random units. Some of the N total may have been ordered in dimers when they entered the crystal; others may have had time to rearrange before the temperature got too low.

The above can be generalized very easily. A particle may introduce a degeneracy in any one of several ways. One is through its orientation, as with CO. Another is through its having several states for rotation (where the molecules still can rotate at almost $0°K$), or several electronic states, all with the same low energy. If the crystal contains N_1 particles of type 1 with particle degeneracy g_1 and N_2 particles of type 2 with particle degeneracy g_2 and so on, then the residual entropy is

$$\bar{S}(0°K) = N_1 k \ln g_1 + N_2 k \ln g_2 + \cdots . \tag{10-7}$$

Examples of residual entropies other than that of CO are plentiful.* Nitrous oxide, N_2O, is a linear molecule and has residual entropy of $Nk \ln 2$. On the other hand, nitric oxide, NO, has experimental residual entropy of $\frac{1}{2}Nk \ln 2$. This indicates that just half as many particles as expected are orienting randomly. One assumes that the NO molecules dimerize before crystallizing out as either

$$\begin{matrix} NO \\ ON \end{matrix} \quad \text{or} \quad \begin{matrix} ON \\ NO \end{matrix} .$$

The crystal of CH_3D has residual entropy of $Nk \ln 4$, since there are four directions in which the deuterium may lie. Hydrogen presents a complicated case, because normal hydrogen is a mixture of three parts of so-called *ortho* hydrogen ($g = 3$) and one part of so-called *para* hydrogen ($g = 1$). Only the $\frac{3}{4}N$ of the molecules that are para hydrogen contribute to the residual entropy $\frac{3}{4}Nk \ln 3$.

PROBLEM

10-1. Consider the residual entropy of carbon monoxide. Inability to predict the precise quantum state at $0°K$ led to a measurable residual entropy. However, one of the *possible* quantum states is the completely ordered one. If, unknown to the experimenter, the system had happened to get into that state, what would the experiment have shown? Does this mean that more heat would have to be added to raise that system to the same final condition as the one in the text? If so, where would the excess heat go? Considered in this light, why should measurements of residual entropies be reproducible?

* An extensive discussion is given by Fowler and Guggenheim, pp. 191–229.

11 GENERAL FORMULATION OF STATISTICAL THERMODYNAMICS

The ensemble average of the energy of a system is given in terms of the partition function in Eq. 9-5, and the entropy is given by Eq. 9-15. One might ask, then, whether it is possible to express the ensemble averages of *all* thermodynamic variables in terms of the partition function. This would reduce the entire problem of statistical thermodynamics to the single one of calculating the partition function.

The basic thermodynamic variables one would like to predict from statistical mechanics are the energy E, the enthalpy H, the Helmholtz free energy A, the Gibbs free energy G, the entropy S, the specific heats C_V and C_P, and the pressure P. With Eqs. 9-5 and 9-15, which already give $\bar{E}$ and $\bar{S}$, the rest of these are easily found.

The easiest starting point in statistical thermodynamics is the Helmholtz free energy:

$$A = E - TS. \tag{11-1}$$

From Eq. 9-15, this is seen to be

$$\bar{A} = \bar{E} - Tk \ln Q - \bar{E},$$

$$\boxed{\bar{A} = -kT \ln Q.} \tag{11-2}$$

This equation is important because it is a simple way to remember the statistical mechanical expressions for the thermodynamic variables. If Eq. 11-2 is remembered, the rest can be derived in the following way:

If a system consisting of N_1 particles of type 1, N_2 particles of type 2, . . . is caused to undergo infinitesimal reversible changes in temperature, volume, and numbers of particles, then the change in Helmholtz free energy is given by

$$dA = \left(\frac{\partial A}{\partial T}\right)_{V,N_i} dT + \left(\frac{\partial A}{\partial V}\right)_{T,N_i} dV + \sum_i \left(\frac{\partial A}{\partial N_i}\right)_{T,V,N_{j \neq i}} dN_i. \tag{11-3}$$

The summation is over all types of constituent particles. The meaning of the symbol $\partial A / \partial N_i$ is the change in A caused by increasing the number of particles of type i from N_i to $N_i + 1$. The meaning of the symbol dN_i is the actual change in the number of particles of type i.

This purely mathematical equation may be compared with its thermodynamic counterpart, one of the so-called *Maxwell relations:*

$$dA = -S \, dT - P \, dV + \sum_i \mu_i \, dN_i. \tag{11-4}$$

The symbol μ_i is the *molecular chemical potential* of the ith constituent. It differs from the molar chemical potential or partial molar free energy customarily used by chemists in being smaller by a factor of Avogadro's number. It is consistently used in this way throughout this book, because the emphasis in statistical mechanics is on the particle nature of matter. Comparing Eq. 11-4 with Eq. 11-3 permits the following identifications, known in thermodynamics as some of the so-called *Gibbs relations:*

$$S = -\left(\frac{\partial A}{\partial T}\right)_{V,N_i}; \quad P = -\left(\frac{\partial A}{\partial V}\right)_{T,N_i}; \quad \mu_i = \left(\frac{\partial A}{\partial N_i}\right)_{T,V,N_{j\neq i}}. \tag{11-5}$$

Coupled with the simple form of $\bar{A}$, Eq. 11-2, Eqs. 11-5 give simple ways to remember $\bar{S}$, $\bar{P}$, and $\bar{\mu}_i$. In addition, Eq. 11-1 gives $\bar{E}$:

$$\bar{E} = \bar{A} + T\bar{S}; \tag{11-6}$$

$\bar{H}$ and $\bar{G}$ are given by their definitions:

$$\bar{H} = \bar{E} + \bar{P}V; \tag{11-7}$$

$$\bar{G} = \bar{H} - T\bar{S} = \bar{A} + \bar{P}V; \tag{11-8}$$

and the heat capacities are given by differentiation:

$$\overline{C_V} = \left(\frac{\partial \bar{E}}{\partial T}\right)_{V,N_i}; \quad \overline{C_P} = \left(\frac{\partial \bar{H}}{\partial T}\right)_{P,N_i}. \tag{11-9}$$

At this point we give a summary of the ensemble averages of the various thermodynamic variables* (see top of next page).

These equations show why the partition function is so widely used to calculate thermodynamic variables from properties of the molecules. Whenever one has a system which is described by a canonical ensemble, if $e^{-\beta E_i}$ may be conveniently summed over all states to yield Q, then the values of all thermodynamic variables follow immediately. Needless to say, this has not solved the problem of equilibrium statistical mechanics. What it has done is to establish a framework, throwing the entire problem into the calculation of the one quantity Q as a function of the variables on which it depends. Of course, finding Q for systems other than ideal

* Note, for any function of temperature $g(T)$,

$$\frac{\partial g}{\partial T} = \frac{\partial g}{\partial \beta}\frac{d\beta}{dT} = \frac{1}{k}\frac{\partial g}{\partial \beta}\frac{d(1/T)}{dT} = -\frac{1}{kT^2}\frac{\partial g}{\partial \beta}.$$

$$\bar{E} = kT^2\left(\frac{\partial \ln Q}{\partial T}\right)_{V,N_i}; \qquad (11\text{-}10)$$

$$\bar{H} = kT^2\left(\frac{\partial \ln Q}{\partial T}\right)_{V,N_i} + kTV\left(\frac{\partial \ln Q}{\partial V}\right)_{T,N_i}; \qquad (11\text{-}11)$$

$$\bar{A} = -kT\ln Q; \qquad (11\text{-}12)$$

$$\bar{G} = -kT\ln Q + kTV\left(\frac{\partial \ln Q}{\partial V}\right)_{T,N_i}; \qquad (11\text{-}13)$$

$$\bar{\mu}_i = -kT\left(\frac{\partial \ln Q}{\partial N_i}\right)_{T,V,N_{j\neq i}}; \qquad (11\text{-}14)$$

$$\bar{S} = k\left[\frac{\partial(T\ln Q)}{\partial T}\right]_{V,N_i} = k\ln Q + \frac{\bar{E}}{T}; \qquad (11\text{-}15)$$

$$\overline{C_V} = \left(\frac{\partial \bar{E}}{\partial T}\right)_{V,N_i}; \qquad (11\text{-}16)$$

$$\overline{C_P} = \left(\frac{\partial \bar{H}}{\partial T}\right)_{P,N_i}; \qquad (11\text{-}17)$$

$$\bar{P} = kT\left(\frac{\partial \ln Q}{\partial V}\right)_{T,N_i}. \qquad (11\text{-}18)$$

gases is by no means easy, and in most cases it represents an unsolved problem. Much of the rest of this book is devoted to studying this problem for various kinds of systems.

PART II

IDEAL GASES

12   THE IDEAL GAS

Introductory presentations of thermodynamics always spend a great deal of time treating the properties of the so-called *ideal gas*. Although no real gases have exactly these properties, there are still good reasons for treating them. The properties of the ideal gas are sufficiently simple that they do not add to the already serious problem of understanding the thermodynamic concepts. Furthermore, the behavior of many real gases approximates that of an ideal gas. Those real gases whose behavior does not are most naturally treated by equations similar to the ones for ideal gases, simply with corrections added for the "degree of non-ideality."

The ideal gas is a hypothetical substance, based on the extrapolated behavior of real gases in the limit of vanishing densities. Many studies of the equations of state of real gases have been made, showing how the pressure P, the temperature T, and the density N/V are related. In the limit of vanishing density, the ratio PV/N for *all* real gases is found to approach $1/\beta$, where β is the thermodynamic integrating factor for the reversible heat, developed in Eq. 9-11:

$$\lim_{\text{density}\to 0} \frac{PV}{N} = \frac{1}{\beta} = kT. \qquad (12\text{-}1)$$

The *scale* of temperature or size of a degree is conventionally determined by studying the left-hand side of Eq. 12-1 for a gas in equilibrium with water at its triple point. Boltzmann's constant k is fixed by the relationship

$$\lim_{\text{density}\to 0} \frac{PV}{N} = (273.1600 \text{ deg})k \qquad (12\text{-}2)$$

for real gases in equilibrium with water at its triple point. The approximate value of k found experimentally is 1.38×10^{-16} erg/deg.

Equations such as these may be written either in terms of molecules or in terms of moles. In the latter case, one employs the universal gas constant R;

$$R = N_0 k, \tag{12-3}$$

where N_0 is Avogadro's number, the number of molecules contained in a mole.

Understanding the ideal gas in terms of molecular theory must be based on an understanding of real gases. Interpretation of experimental data has led to the following picture of real gas molecules: In general, molecules are objects which interact with each other. At fairly large distances, two

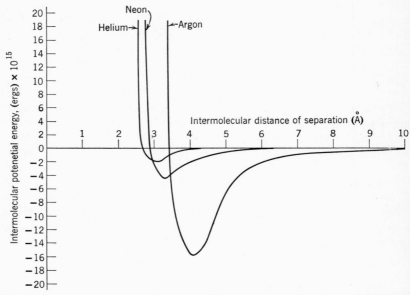

Fig. 12-1. Potential energy curves for He, Ne, A. (From Hirschfelder, Curtiss, and Bird, pp. 197–199.)

neutral molecules almost always attract each other. At closer distances they repel each other. It is convenient to represent the intermolecular force as the negative of the slope of a plot of intermolecular potential energy against distance of separation. In Fig. 12-1 this is done for typical pairs of helium, neon, and argon atoms. Most pairs of molecules interact in a similar manner. As real molecules approach each other, their mutual potential energy becomes smaller; the force acting on them, the slope of the potential curve, is attractive. At a certain distance of separation, the potential energy is a minimum; there is then no force between them. As they come closer, their mutual potential energy increases sharply; thus they repel each other strongly at small distances of separation.

Real gases approach ideal behavior in the limit of vanishing density. As the density is decreased, the number of pairs of molecules close enough to interact appreciably (say, within 10 Å of each other) gets smaller. Finally, in the limit of vanishing density, the number of molecules within each others' fields of force is completely negligible. The fact that molecules interact with each other has no bearing on the properties of a gas in that limit.

We therefore choose to define an ideal gas an one in which the molecular interactions through intermolecular forces are ignored. Since the intermolecular potential energy is neglected, the entire energy of the system is contained in the kinetic and internal energies of the particles themselves. Under the conditions cited in Sec. 8 for the validity of exponential reduced distribution functions, this mechanical picture is shown in Sec. 13 to lead to the two properties of an ideal gas often cited in thermodynamics books:

1. The molar energy of a given gas is a function only of the temperature and not of the volume:

$$E = E(T), \quad \text{or} \quad \left(\frac{\partial E}{\partial V}\right)_T = 0. \tag{12-4}$$

2. The thermal equation of state is

$$PV = NkT. \tag{12-5}$$

13   CLASSICAL GAS—
TRANSLATIONAL ENERGY AND PRESSURE

In Secs. 13 to 16 a classical mechanical picture is used to learn a surprising amount about ideal gases. It is true that quantum mechanics actually governs molecular dynamics, and the quantum treatment of Secs. 17 to 19 duplicates some of Secs. 13 to 16. Nevertheless, the classical picture gives considerable physical insight. Also, it resembles more closely the type of argument the reader will encounter if he ever studies non-equilibrium statistical mechanics, where the partition function is useless and physical insight vital.*

In this section, the classical ensemble for describing the translation of molecules is discussed and the resulting one-particle distribution function is described in some detail. The normalized distribution function is found. When this is used, the ensemble average of the translational energy of a particle is found to be $\frac{3}{2}kT$. The energy of the system is seen to be a function only of T, not of V, as is required by Eq. 12-4. Furthermore, the ensemble average of the pressure is also obtained, yielding precisely Eq. 12-5 as equation of state if β is equated to $1/kT$. This identifies, through statistical mechanics, the absolute thermodynamic temperature of Eq. 9-12 with the ideal gas temperature, and it identifies the constant k of Eq. 9-12 with Boltzmann's constant, obtained experimentally from Eq. 12-2.

THE CLASSICAL ONE-PARTICLE DISTRIBUTION FUNCTION

In a classical ensemble, ignoring the internal structure of the molecules, the parameters describing one particle are the three position coordinates and the three momentum coordinates. For brevity these are written as vectors **r** and **p** respectively.† Since these parameters are continuous, a one-particle *distribution function* of the form treated in Eqs. 4-22 to 4-29 is needed. The joint probability that some particle of interest has its x coordinate between x and $x + dx$, *and* has its y coordinate between y and $y + dy$, *and* has its z coordinate between z and $z + dz$, *and* has its momentum component in the x direction between p_x and $p_x + dp_x$, *and* has its momentum component in the y direction between p_y and $p_y + dp_y$, *and* has its momentum component in the z direction between p_z and $p_z + dp_z$ is

$$f_1(x, y, z, p_x, p_y, p_z)\, dx\, dy\, dz\, dp_x\, dp_y\, dp_z. \tag{13-1}$$

The subscript on f_1 refers to the fact that knowledge of f_1 as a function of the variables on which it depends gives full information about a *single* particle. Usually, f_1 is called the **one-particle distribution function,** sometimes the *singlet distribution function.*

---

* Certain aspects of this classical mechanical study are frequently referred to as the *kinetic theory of gases,* but different people use the phrase with different meanings. Because of this lack of agreement, the phrase *kinetic theory* is not used in this book.
† In this book, boldface letters refer to vectors. The origin of position vectors is arbitrary and may be taken to be one corner of the box holding the system. The origin of momentum or velocity vectors is chosen naturally by the momentum or velocity of the system as a whole.

For brevity, one often finds use made of the following conventional way of writing volume elements:

$$dx\, dy\, dz = d\mathbf{r}; \quad dp_x\, dp_y\, dp_z = d\mathbf{p}. \tag{13-2}$$

When boldface is used for only the last part of the differential, it does not imply vector character. Instead it simply indicates a three-dimensional differential. In this notation, Eq. 13-1 is

$$f_1(\mathbf{r}, \mathbf{p})\, d\mathbf{r}\, d\mathbf{p}. \tag{13-3}$$

Before putting f_1 to use, we shall give a brief review of its meaning. We are interested in a certain particle, say, particle i. In Figs. 13-1 and

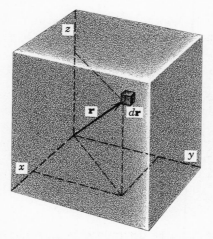

Fig. 13-1. Configuration space of one particle.

13-2, the configuration and momentum spaces for particle i are illustrated. Together they form the complete phase space of particle i, as discussed in Sec. 5. Configuration space is limited to the interior of a box of volume V. Momentum space, however, is virtually unlimited. Vectors $\mathbf{r}$ and $\mathbf{p}$ have been drawn arbitrarily in Figs. 13-1 and 13-2, and at their ends volume elements $d\mathbf{r}$ and $d\mathbf{p}$ have been indicated.

The ensemble, on which the probability theory is based, has each member with a definite position and momentum for each particle. For a given choice of $\mathbf{r}$, $\mathbf{p}$, $d\mathbf{r}$, and $d\mathbf{p}$, one can just look and see what fraction of the members has particle i inside the volume element $d\mathbf{r}$ and has a momentum vector for particle i whose tip lies inside $d\mathbf{p}$. This fraction is

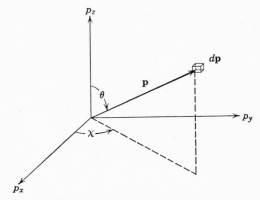

Fig. 13-2. Momentum space of one particle.

the probability, Eq. 13-3, for that choice of $\mathbf{r}$, $\mathbf{p}$, $d\mathbf{r}$, and $d\mathbf{p}$. The ensemble therefore defines the one-particle distribution function $f_1(\mathbf{r}, \mathbf{p})$.

NORMALIZED EXPONENTIAL DISTRIBUTION

Sections 13 to 16 stay within the restrictions laid down in Sec. 8 for the validity of exponential reduced probabilities. It is shown in Secs. 17 and 22 that this is a useful procedure for almost any common substance one would ordinarily call a "gas." There is nothing in Secs. 6 to 8 to limit the results to quantum mechanics except the use of discrete probabilities. The same analysis applied to the complete distribution function for a classical ensemble would show that under the restrictions of Sec. 8

$$f_1(\mathbf{r}, \mathbf{p}) = \alpha e^{-\beta \epsilon(\mathbf{r}, \mathbf{p})}. \tag{13-4}$$

where α is a constant to be determined by normalization, and ϵ is the energy of a particle located at $\mathbf{r}$ if its momentum is $\mathbf{p}$. This energy is the sum of the potential energy of the particle with respect to external fields and the kinetic energy of the particle due to its motion. The problem of external fields is considered in Sec. 21. The physical content of Eq. 13-4 is exactly the same as that of Eq. 8-1.

For the case treated here, ϵ is simply the kinetic energy of the particle $p^2/2m$:

$$f_1(\mathbf{r}, \mathbf{p}) = \alpha e^{-\beta p^2/2m}. \tag{13-5}$$

There is no dependence on $\mathbf{r}$. The constant α is found from the normalization condition, analogous to Eq. 4-25:

$$\int d\mathbf{r} \, d\mathbf{p} \, \alpha e^{-\beta p^2/2m} = 1. \tag{13-6}$$

Since there is no **r**-dependence in the integrand, integration over $d\mathbf{r}$ yields simply the factor V:

$$V\alpha \int d\mathbf{p}\, e^{-\beta p^2/2m} = 1, \qquad (13\text{-}7)$$

$$V\alpha \int_{-\infty}^{\infty} dp_x \int_{-\infty}^{\infty} dp_y \int_{-\infty}^{\infty} dp_z e^{-\beta(p_x^2 + p_y^2 + p_z^2)/2m} = 1,$$

$$V\alpha \left(\frac{2\pi m}{\beta}\right)^{3/2} = 1. \qquad (13\text{-}8)$$

The value of the integral is given in Appendix C, Eq. C-1. Equation 13-8 may be solved for α and this value used in Eq. 13-5:

$$\alpha = \frac{1}{V}\left(\frac{\beta}{2\pi m}\right)^{3/2}, \qquad (13\text{-}9)$$

$$\boxed{f_1(\mathbf{r}, \mathbf{p}) = \frac{1}{V}\left(\frac{\beta}{2\pi m}\right)^{3/2} e^{-\beta p^2/2m}.} \qquad (13\text{-}10)$$

The $1/V$ term in α is the reciprocal of the volume available to a particle in configuration space. The $\beta/2\pi m$ term may be thought of as the reciprocal of the available volume in momentum space.

AVERAGE ENERGY OF A PARTICLE

Knowing f_1, it is an easy matter to find the ensemble average of the translational energy of a single particle. In analogy with Eq. 4-26 and Prob. 4-5, this average is

$$\bar{\epsilon}_{\text{trans}} = \int d\mathbf{r}\, d\mathbf{p}\, \epsilon(\mathbf{r}, \mathbf{p}) f_1(\mathbf{r}, \mathbf{p})$$

$$= \int d\mathbf{r}\, d\mathbf{p}\, \frac{p^2}{2m}\frac{1}{V}\left(\frac{\beta}{2\pi m}\right)^{3/2} e^{-\beta p^2/2m},$$

$$\bar{\epsilon}_{\text{trans}} = \frac{1}{2m}\left(\frac{\beta}{2\pi m}\right)^{3/2} \int d\mathbf{p}\, p^2 e^{-\beta p^2/2m}. \qquad (13\text{-}11)$$

Again, the configurational integral yields simply the factor V. There are several ways to integrate Eq. 13-11. One is presented in Prob. 13-4. Another is to express $d\mathbf{p}$ in spherical coordinates, referring to Fig. 13-2:

$$d\mathbf{p} = dp_x\, dp_y\, dp_z = p^2\, dp \sin\theta\, d\theta\, d\chi; \qquad (13\text{-}12)$$

$$\bar{\epsilon}_{\text{trans}} = \frac{1}{2m}\left(\frac{\beta}{2\pi m}\right)^{3/2} \int_0^{\infty} p^2\, dp \int_0^{\pi} \sin\theta\, d\theta \int_0^{2\pi} d\chi\, p^2 e^{-\beta p^2/2m}.$$

Since the integrand is not a function of θ or χ, the integrations over angles yield simply 2 and 2π respectively:

$$\bar{\epsilon}_{trans} = \frac{2\pi}{m}\left(\frac{\beta}{2\pi m}\right)^{3/2} \int_0^\infty p^4 e^{-\beta p^2/2m}\, dp$$

$$= \frac{2\pi}{m}\left(\frac{\beta}{2\pi m}\right)^{3/2} \frac{3\pi^{1/2}}{8}\left(\frac{2m}{\beta}\right)^{5/2},$$

$$\boxed{\bar{\epsilon}_{trans} = \frac{3}{2\beta} = \tfrac{3}{2}kT.} \tag{13-13}$$

This result is very simple: The ensemble average of the translational energy of a single particle is $\tfrac{3}{2}kT$. The result is not only independent of volume, but it is also independent of the mass of the gas molecules. For example, in an equilibrium mixture of helium and argon, the average kinetic energy per particle is the same regardless of the kind of particle. For a system composed of N particles,

$$\bar{E}_{trans} = \tfrac{3}{2}NkT. \tag{13-14}$$

This expression for $\bar{E}_{trans}$ satisfies the requirement of Eq. 12-4. Furthermore, if the *internal* energies of the particles were included in $\bar{E}$,

$$\bar{E} = \bar{E}_{trans} + \bar{E}_{int}, \tag{13-15}$$

there still would be no volume dependence, because there is nothing in the internal energies that has anything to do with the volume. The contributions from the internal energies are discussed in Secs. 16 and 19.

THE PRESSURE AND EQUATION OF STATE

The first problem in computing the pressure in an ideal gas is to visualize the macroscopic pressure in terms of the motions of the gas molecules. The pressure in any particular region of the gas is defined as the force the gas molecules would exert on a surface of unit area located in that region. The force is normal to the surface, and since force is time rate of change of momentum, the pressure may be written

$$P = \frac{\text{force normal to surface}}{\text{area of surface}}$$
$$= \frac{\text{time rate of change of } \mathbf{p} \text{ normal to surface}}{\text{area of surface}}. \tag{13-16}$$

Let the area A be the top side of a surface located in the gas perpendicular to the z axis. Every particle approaching A from the plus z side will rebound after striking A. The p_x and p_y components of momentum of those particles will be unchanged if the collisions are elastic but the p_z component will be changed in sign:

$$p_x \to p_x, \text{ regardless of } p_x;$$

$$p_y \to p_y, \text{ regardless of } p_y;$$

$$-p_z \to p_z, p_z \text{ must be negative.}$$

Clearly, p_z must be negative, because molecules with positive p_z would

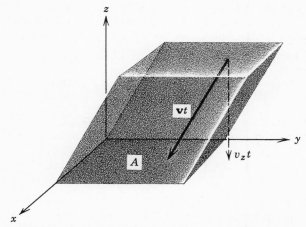

Fig. 13-3. Parallelepiped of impact for a particular edge, $\mathbf{v}t = \mathbf{p}t/m$.

be headed away from A. Each collision gives a change in momentum of

$$\Delta p = p_{\text{after coll}} - p_{\text{before coll}} = 2p_z. \tag{13-17}$$

The total pressure one will predict is N times the average contribution to Eq. 13-16 from a particular molecule, say, particle i. The question is, when we look at a member of the ensemble, how can we tell whether particle i will strike A from above during the next time interval t? Clearly, the answer is that particle i will strike A from above if it is within the parallelepiped which has A as its base and its edges given by the distance it travels during time t, $\mathbf{v}t$, or $\mathbf{p}t/m$. This is illustrated by Fig. 13-3. Since there is a different parallelepiped for each velocity, the volume of the parallelepiped is a function of velocity. It is the area of the base times the height $p_z t/m$. Therefore, the volume τ within which particle i must be if it is to strike

A from above during the time t, is

$$\tau = \frac{Ap_z t}{m}.$$ (13-18)

Now Eq. 13-16 may be used to calculate the ensemble average of the contribution to the pressure made by particle i, $\overline{P(i)}$. This is simply $1/A$ times the average of the time rate of change of momentum caused by collisions of particle i with A. It is, therefore, $1/A$ times the average of the change of momentum during the time t, divided by t. The momentum change for each collision is $2p_z$. The ensemble average is therefore $2p_z$ times $f_1(\mathbf{r}, \mathbf{p})$ integrated over those positions and momenta that lead to collisions. Since particle i must be in the volume τ if it is to collide with A, the configuration integral is only over the volume τ. Since τ is a function of momentum, this integral must be performed before the momentum integrals. The limits on the momentum integrals are unrestricted for p_x and p_y but p_z must of course be negative:

$$\overline{P(i)} = \frac{1}{At} \int_{-\infty}^{\infty} dp_x \int_{-\infty}^{\infty} dp_y \int_{-\infty}^{0} dp_z \int_{\tau} d\mathbf{r}\, 2p_z f_1(\mathbf{r}, \mathbf{p})$$ (13-19)

$$= \frac{1}{At} \int_{-\infty}^{\infty} dp_x \int_{-\infty}^{\infty} dp_y \int_{-\infty}^{0} dp_z \tau\, 2p_z f_1(\mathbf{r}, \mathbf{p})$$

$$= \frac{2}{m} \int_{-\infty}^{\infty} dp_x \int_{-\infty}^{\infty} dp_y \int_{-\infty}^{0} dp_z p_z^2 \frac{1}{V} \left(\frac{\beta}{2\pi m}\right)^{3/2} e^{-\beta p^2/2m}.$$

Since the integrand in Eq. 13-19 is independent of $\mathbf{r}$, the configuration integral simply gives the volume τ in which particle i must be. The momentum integrals are easily evaluated using Appendix C:

$$\overline{P(i)} = \frac{2}{mV} \left(\frac{\beta}{2\pi m}\right)^{3/2} \int_{-\infty}^{\infty} dp_x \int_{-\infty}^{\infty} dp_y \int_{-\infty}^{0} dp_z p_z^2 e^{-\beta(p_x^2 + p_y^2 + p_z^2)/2m}$$

$$= \frac{2}{mV} \left(\frac{\beta}{2\pi m}\right)^{3/2} \pi^{1/2} \left(\frac{2m}{\beta}\right)^{1/2} \pi^{1/2} \left(\frac{2m}{\beta}\right)^{1/2} \frac{\pi^{1/2}}{4} \left(\frac{2m}{\beta}\right)^{3/2},$$

$$\overline{P(i)} = \frac{1}{V\beta}.$$ (13-20)

Since each particle contributes as much to the ensemble average of the pressure as does particle i, the total pressure predicted for an ideal gas is

$$\boxed{\bar{P} = \frac{N}{V\beta}.}$$ (13-21)

This establishes the equation of state of the ideal gas by statistical mechanics. Comparison of Eq. 13-21 with Eq. 12-4 shows them to be identical;

$$PV = NkT \tag{13-22}$$

if

$$\beta = \frac{1}{kT}. \tag{13-23}$$

Thus, statistical mechanics has shown that the ideal gas temperature as given by Eq. 13-22 is identical to the thermodynamic absolute temperature of Eq. 9-12. Use of Eqs. 9-11 and 9-12 or Eq. 13-22, with k determined experimentally from Eq. 12-2, fixes the absolute temperature.

PROBLEMS

13-1. In deriving Eq. 13-8, use was made of Eq. C-1. Prove Eq. C-1 from elementary integrals.

13-2. In deriving Eq. 13-13, use was made of Eq. C-5. Prove Eq. C-5 from elementary integrals.

13-3. In deriving Eq. 13-20, use was made of Eq. C-3. Prove Eq. C-3 from elementary integrals.

13-4. Derive Eq. 13-13 from Eq. 13-11 by performing the momentum integration in Cartesian coordinates, not spherical.

14   CLASSICAL GAS— MOLECULAR VELOCITIES

In this section, the probability distribution functions for momentum, velocity, and speed (magnitude of velocity) are studied for the molecules in an ideal gas.

For the ideal gas in the absence of external fields, the one-particle distribution function, Eq. 13-10, is independent of the position of the particle **r**. The interesting information contained in Eq. 13-10 is the probabilities of various values of the momentum of particle i. For many purposes, the reduced one-particle momentum or velocity distribution function gives the desired information. The **one-particle momentum**

distribution function $\varphi_1(\mathbf{p})$ is given by

$$\varphi_1(\mathbf{p}) = \int d\mathbf{r}\, f_1(\mathbf{r}, \mathbf{p}). \qquad (14\text{-}1)$$

The meaning of φ_1 is the following: The probability that the momentum of particle i lies within $d\mathbf{p}$ at $\mathbf{p}$ is given by $\varphi_1(\mathbf{p})\, d\mathbf{p}$ (see Fig. 13-2). The momentum distribution is in the complete three-dimensional momentum space of one particle; the meaning of $d\mathbf{p}$ is the product $dp_x\, dp_y\, dp_z$.

In the case of equilibrium, φ_1 is found by integrating Eq. 13-10 over positions:

$$\varphi_1(\mathbf{p}) = \int d\mathbf{r}\, \frac{1}{V}\left(\frac{1}{2\pi mkT}\right)^{3/2} e^{-p^2/2mkT},$$

$$\varphi_1(\mathbf{p}) = \left(\frac{1}{2\pi mkT}\right)^{3/2} e^{-p^2/2mkT}. \qquad (14\text{-}2)$$

Momenta are less easily visualized than velocities. For non-relativistic speeds, $\mathbf{p} = m\mathbf{v}$ converts from one to the other. The **one-particle velocity distribution function** $\Phi_1(\mathbf{v})$ may be defined by the following statement: The probability that the velocity of particle i lies within $d\mathbf{v}$ at $\mathbf{v}$ is given by $\Phi_1(\mathbf{v})\, d\mathbf{v}$. Because of the correspondence between momenta and velocities, the differential probabilities that define them may be equated in order to find how Φ_1 differs from φ_1:

$$\varphi_1(\mathbf{p})\, d\mathbf{p} = \Phi_1(\mathbf{v})\, d\mathbf{v}, \qquad (14\text{-}3)$$

$$\varphi_1(\mathbf{p}) m^3\, d\mathbf{v} = \Phi_1(\mathbf{v})\, d\mathbf{v},$$

$$\Phi_1(\mathbf{v}) = m^3\, \varphi_1(\mathbf{p}); \qquad (14\text{-}4)$$

$$\boxed{\Phi_1(\mathbf{v}) = \left(\frac{m}{2\pi kT}\right)^{3/2} e^{-mv^2/2kT}.} \qquad (14\text{-}5)$$

The m^3 arose from the fact that $dp_x = m\, dv_x$, and $d\mathbf{p} = dp_x\, dp_y\, dp_z$. The reader may check to see that Eq. 14-5 is properly normalized. The result given by Eq. 14-5 is called the **Maxwell velocity distribution.**

The Maxwell distribution gives the probabilities of different velocities for a particular particle. Since, however, there is nothing sacred about any one particle, the same distribution holds for each particle. It is customary to visualize Eq. 14-5 as giving the distribution of the actual velocities that exist among the N gas molecules in the system. This is a useful insight because of the enormous size of N. It must be emphasized, however, that Φ_1 is only a probability distribution; we do not *know* what the distribution of velocities in the system actually is.

It is interesting to consider $\Phi_1(\mathbf{v})$ graphically. Since three dimensions pose a problem, we study $\Phi(v_x)$, the distribution function for the x component of velocity,

$$\Phi(v_x) = \left(\frac{m}{2\pi kT}\right)^{1/2} e^{-mv_x^2/2kT}, \tag{14-6}$$

defined by the following statement: The probability that the x component of velocity of particle i lies between v_x and $v_x + dv_x$ is given by $\Phi(v_x)\,dv_x$. A plot of $\Phi(v_x)$ against v_x gives the familiar bell-shaped curve shown in Fig. 14-1.

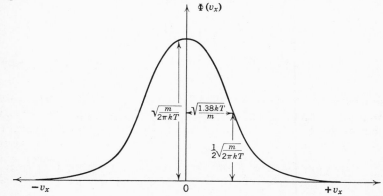

Fig. 14-1. Plot of distribution function for x component of velocity $\Phi(v_x)$ versus v_x, as given by Eq. 14-6.

Several things may be noted: The most probable velocity is zero. At zero, $\Phi(0)$ is $\sqrt{m/2\pi kT}$. The curve is symmetric about $v_x = 0$, so both positive and negative velocities are equally probable. The *average* velocity in the x direction $\bar{v}_x$ is clearly zero. If this were not so and the average particle were moving, the entire box of gas would have to be moving along the table (or floor). Although we have singled out $\Phi(v_x)$, the distributions $\Phi(v_y)$ and $\Phi(v_z)$ are identical in all respects.

The area under the curve of Fig. 14-1 between any two values of v_x is the probability that the particle examined will have its x component of velocity someplace between the two limits. The total area under the curve must of course be unity, since $\Phi(v_x)$ is normalized.

In Fig. 14-2, curves similar to the one in Fig. 14-1 are shown for three different temperatures, $T_1 < T_2 < T_3$, to show how these features remain true as the temperature changes. As was indicated in Fig. 14-1, and as the reader will verify in Prob. 14-1, $\Phi(v_x)$ has decreased to half its maximum value at $v_x = \pm\sqrt{1.38kT/m}$. Therefore, at low temperatures, molecular

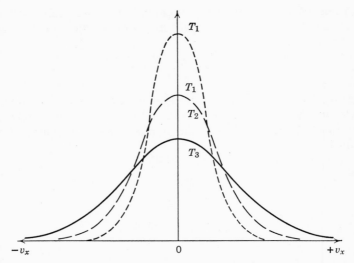

Fig. 14-2. Plot similar to Fig. 14-1 except for three different temperatures T_1, $T_2 = 2T_1$, $T_3 = 4T_1$.

velocities are more clustered about zero. As the temperature is increased, fewer particles have low velocities and correspondingly more have high velocities.

Since Eq. 14-5 is spherically symmetric, distributions of the form of Figs. 14-1 and 14-2 hold regardless of the direction chosen for the x axis. This book always treats velocity as a directed or vector quantity. Since there is no preferred direction for the particle velocity, $\bar{\mathbf{v}}$ is zero. Often, this distribution is not so interesting as is the distribution of molecular speeds. In this book the word *speed* is always used for the magnitude of

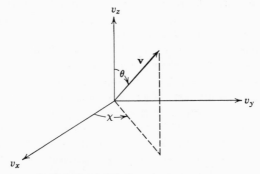

Fig. 14-3. Velocity vector for one particle.

the velocity vector. The speed v is given by

$$v = |\mathbf{v}| = \sqrt{v_x^2 + v_y^2 + v_z^2} = \sqrt{v^2}. \tag{14-7}$$

The velocity vector may be characterized by a magnitude and two angles, just like the momentum was in Fig. 13-2. This is shown in Fig. 14-3.

The Maxwell distribution depends only on v^2 and not on θ or χ. Therefore, $\Phi_1(\mathbf{v})$ may be reduced still further to a distribution of speeds in the ensemble by integration over angles. The **one-particle speed distribution function** $\phi(v)$ is defined as follows: The probability that the speed of particle i lies between v and $v + dv$ is given by $\phi(v)\, dv$. This is obtained by integrating $\Phi_1(\mathbf{v})\, d\mathbf{v}$ over angles:

$$\phi(v)\, dv = \int_{\text{angles}} \Phi_1(\mathbf{v})\, d\mathbf{v}$$

$$= \int_{\text{angles}} \Phi_1(\mathbf{v})v^2\, dv \sin \theta\, d\theta\, d\chi$$

$$= \left(\frac{m}{2\pi kT}\right)^{3/2} e^{-mv^2/2kT}v^2\, dv \int_0^{\pi} \sin \theta\, d\theta \int_0^{2\pi} d\chi$$

$$= 4\pi \left(\frac{m}{2\pi kT}\right)^{3/2} e^{-mv^2/2kT}v^2\, dv.$$

Therefore,

$$\boxed{\phi(v) = 4\pi \left(\frac{m}{2\pi kT}\right)^{3/2} v^2 e^{-mv^2/2kT}.} \tag{14-8}$$

The form of the speed distribution $\phi(v)$ differs from that of the velocity distribution $\Phi_1(\mathbf{v})$ in its normalization constant and in the presence of the v^2 multiplying the exponential. Speeds, of course, are always positive. In Fig. 14-4, $\phi(v)$ is plotted against v. The humped shape of the curve in Fig. 14-4 results from the fact that $\phi(v)$ is the product of two factors, the exponential, which drops off like the right half of Fig. 14-1, and v^2, which increases. For a while the increasing v^2 dominates the decreasing exponential and $\phi(v)$ increases. Then the decreasing exponential more than damps the v^2.

The area under the curve of Fig. 14-4 between any two values of v is the probability that the particle examined will have its speed someplace between the two limits. The total area under the curve must of course be unity, since $\phi(v)$ is normalized.

While the most probable value of the *velocity* is zero, the likelihood of zero *speed* is negligible. A zero speed demands that all three components of velocity be precisely zero, and this occurs a vanishing number of times.

It is easy to find the value of v for which $\phi(v)$ is a maximum. This is the

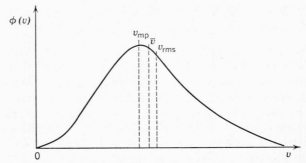

Fig. 14-4. Plot of distribution function for speed $\phi(v)$ versus v, as given by Eq. 14-8.

most probable value v_{mp} **of the speed** of the particle being examined. It is found most easily by noting that ϕ is a function of v^2 and may be maximized with respect to v^2:

$$\frac{d\phi}{dv^2} = 4\pi \left(\frac{m}{2\pi kT}\right)^{3/2} \left(-\frac{m}{2kT} v^2 e^{-mv^2/2kT} + e^{-mv^2/2kT}\right) = 0.$$

Therefore,

$$-\frac{m}{2kT} v_{\mathrm{mp}}^2 + 1 = 0,$$

$$v_{\mathrm{mp}}^2 = \frac{2kT}{m},$$

$$\boxed{v_{\mathrm{mp}} = \sqrt{2}\sqrt{kT/m} = \sqrt{2}\sqrt{RT/M}.} \qquad (14\text{-}9)$$

The symbol M is used for the *molecular weight*, that is, for the weight of Avogadro's number of particles;

$$M = N_0 m. \qquad (14\text{-}10)$$

The **ensemble average** $\bar{v}$ **of the speed of a particle** is found in the usual way, as given by Eq. 4-26:

$$\bar{v} = \int_0^\infty v\,\phi(v)\,dv$$

$$= \int_0^\infty 4\pi \left(\frac{m}{2\pi kT}\right)^{3/2} v^3 e^{-mv^2/2kT}\,dv$$

$$= 4\pi \left(\frac{m}{2\pi kT}\right)^{3/2} \frac{(2kT)^2}{2m^2},$$

$$\boxed{\bar{v} = \sqrt{8/\pi}\sqrt{kT/m} = \sqrt{8/\pi}\sqrt{RT/M}.} \qquad (14\text{-}11)$$

The integral is given in Appendix C, Eq. C-4.

Often, as was seen in Sec. 13, the quantity of interest is the *ensemble average of the square of the velocity or speed:*

$$\overline{v^2} = \int_0^\infty v^2\,\phi(v)\,dv$$

$$= \int_0^\infty 4\pi\left(\frac{m}{2\pi kT}\right)^{3/2} v^4 e^{-mv^2/2kT}\,dv$$

$$= 4\pi\left(\frac{m}{2\pi kT}\right)^{3/2}\frac{3\pi^{1/2}}{8}\left(\frac{2kT}{m}\right)^{5/2},$$

$$\overline{v^2} = \frac{3kT}{m} = \frac{3RT}{M}. \tag{14-12}$$

This proof differs only slightly from that of Eq. 13-13:

$$\bar{\epsilon}_{\text{trans}} = \tfrac{1}{2}m\overline{v^2} = \tfrac{3}{2}kT, \tag{14-13}$$

a form in which Eq. 14-12 may easily be remembered. In order to compare $\overline{v^2}$ with v_{mp} and $\bar{v}$, its square root is taken and called the **root mean square velocity** v_{rms}:

$$\boxed{v_{\text{rms}} = \sqrt{\overline{v^2}} = \sqrt{3}\,\sqrt{kT/m} = \sqrt{3}\,\sqrt{RT/M}.} \tag{14-14}$$

The reader may quickly verify that the molecules in air at ordinary temperatures have average speeds of from 10^4 to 10^5 cm/sec.

Thus, there are three commonly used measures of average speeds in a gas. It is interesting to compare the three values v_{mp}, $\bar{v}$, and v_{rms}:

$$v_{\text{mp}}:\bar{v}:v_{\text{rms}}::\sqrt{2}:\sqrt{8/\pi}:\sqrt{3} = 1.41:1.59:1.73. \tag{14-15}$$

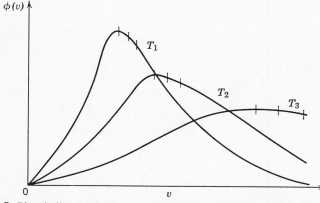

Fig. 14-5. Plot similar to Fig. 14-4 except for three different temperatures T_1, $T_2 = 2T_1$, $T_3 = 4T_1$.

Figure 14-5 shows how these features of the speed distribution change with temperature. As the temperature is increased, the three averages v_{mp}, $\bar{v}$, and v_{rms} increase as $\sqrt{T}$. Furthermore, the clustering of expected velocities about the most probable becomes less pronounced at higher temperatures, because increased speeds become more likely. The temperature is clearly a measure of the average speed, and, of course, from Eq. 14-13, of the average kinetic energy per gas molecule.

PROBLEMS

14-1. Prove that $\Phi(v_x)$ has decreased to half its maximum value at $v_x = \pm\sqrt{1.38\,kT/m}$.

14-2. In deriving Eq. 14-11, use was made of Eq. C-4. Prove Eq. C-4 from elementary integrals.

14-3. In a mixture of H_2 and O_2, what is the ratio of $v_{rms}(H_2)$ to $v_{rms}(O_2)$? What is the same ratio of $\bar{v}$'s? Of v_{mp}'s?

14-4. Calculate $\bar{v}$ for hydrogen and nitrogen gases at 25°C.

14-5. What fraction of members of the ensemble have particle i with *kinetic energy* between κ and $\kappa + d\kappa$? What kinetic energy is the most probable?

14-6. What interpretation should be given to the following velocity distribution, in which a, b, and c are constants:

$$\Phi_1(v) = \left(\frac{m}{2\pi kT}\right)^{3/2} \exp\left\{-\frac{m}{2kT}\left[(v_x - a)^2 + (v_y - b)^2 + (v_z - c)^2\right]\right\}?$$

14-7. If an atom is radiating light of wave length λ_0 and that atom is moving away from the observer at a rate of v_z cm/sec, the observer sees the light at wave length

$$\lambda = \lambda_0\left(1 + \frac{v_z}{c}\right),$$

because of the Doppler effect. The factor c is the velocity of light. If a gas at temperature T emits at λ_0, an observer looking at the gas from some distance away (far enough that all light rays reaching him are essentially parallel) will see the line at λ_0 fuzzed because of the variety of Doppler shifts. If $I(\lambda)\,d\lambda$ is the intensity of illumination the observer sees with wave length between λ and $\lambda + d\lambda$, what is the predicted dependence of $I(\lambda)$ on λ in terms of I, where I is the *total* intensity the observer sees? Sketch a plot of $I(\lambda)$ versus λ.

14-8. The "error function of x," abbreviated erf x, is defined by

$$\text{erf } x = \frac{2}{\sqrt{\pi}}\int_0^x e^{-z^2}\,dz.$$

In terms of error functions, what fraction of gas molecules has x components of velocity between $+2\sqrt{2kT/m}$ and $-2\sqrt{2kT/m}$?

14-9. Suppose the system was isolated with fixed energy and contained only three particles. Discuss how this would affect Fig. 14.1.

14-10. What is the speed in kilometers per second at which $\Phi_1(v)$ takes just half its maximum value for nitrogen molecules at 25°C? Compare with v_{mp}. How can the most probable speed be greater than the speed which damps $\Phi_1(v)$ to half its maximum value?

15

CLASSICAL GAS—
MOLECULAR TRAJECTORIES

In the last section and in this one, the probable behavior of individual molecules is studied in order to get an idea of how the molecules are behaving in the system. For macroscopic gaseous systems, predictions properly based on such a theory have consistently agreed with observed physical phenomena. In Sec. 14, the velocity of molecules in an ideal gas was the feature of the particle behavior that was studied. In this section, some features involving the trajectories of the particles are considered.

It is often of interest to know how many collisions with other molecules a typical molecule undergoes during a unit of time. From this, knowing the speed of the molecule, it is possible to calculate the average length of the paths between collisions. This type of problem is considered here, but actually, it is misleading to discuss molecular collisions in an *ideal* gas. If the intermolecular forces are to be neglected completely, as they must for the gas to be ideal, then how does one know what a collision is? We shall just have to assume that collisions are rare enough in the gas that it is still reasonable to neglect the effect of intermolecular potential energy in all calculations.

THE COLLISION CROSS-SECTION

For a given process, a molecule of type 1 is characterized by a **collision cross-section** s_{21} with molecules of type 2. The collision cross-section is the effective area that a molecule of type 1 would present to a molecule

Fig. 15-1. The collision cross-section s_{21} presented to particle 2 by particle 1 as they pass each other.

of type 2 as the two molecules moved by each other. The smaller s_{21}, the closer together the two particles' centers must come before they collide. If the center of particle 2 comes within some small distance of the center of particle 1, the two particles may be said to have collided. If the particles are hard spheres, the definition of a collision is an easy matter, but for general intermolecular potentials, like those pictured in Fig. 12-1, this is not so simple. In Fig. 15-1, the concept of collision cross-section is illustrated. The area s_{21} is at right angles to the velocity which particle 2 has as seen by a person riding on particle 1. If particle 2 crosses this area, a collision has occurred, and the particles very likely are deflected. If it misses the area, there is no collision.

We have pointed out that s_{21} is a property not only of the types of colliding molecules, but also of the particular process under consideration. What may act like a collision in a process of molecular diffusion may not in a process of heat conduction. What may act like a collision in heat conduction may not be one in the process that leads to viscosity. In this book, these transport phenomena are not studied, and a simple view of s_{21} is taken. *For example*, for the special case of a single-component gas of hard sphere molecules of *diameter* σ, the collision cross-section quite unambiguously is $\pi\sigma^2$, since if the center of molecule 2 comes within σ of the center of molecule 1 there is a collision. This is illustrated by Fig. 15-2.

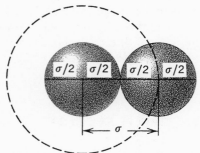

Fig. 15-2. Grazing collision of two hard spheres. Dotted circle is collision cross-section $\pi\sigma^2$ if σ is molecular diameter.

THE RELATIVE VELOCITY

In the collision process, it is clearly the velocity of particle 2 *relative to that of particle* 1 which is important:

$$\mathbf{v}_{21} = \mathbf{v}_2 - \mathbf{v}_1. \tag{15-1}$$

If a person were sitting on top of particle 1, he would see particle 2 moving with velocity $\mathbf{v}_{21}$. The difference between $\mathbf{v}_2$ and $\mathbf{v}_{21}$ is that the vector $\mathbf{v}_2$ has an origin which is at rest with respect to the laboratory, whereas $\mathbf{v}_{21}$ has as its origin the velocity of particle 1, which varies from member to member in the ensemble.

Fig. 15-3. Volume an observer sitting on particle 1 sees particle 2 sweep out during t seconds, $sv_{21}t$.

Now, suppose one were sitting on molecule 1, watching molecule 2 move through space. If the collision cross-section is s, the collision volume one would see particle 2 sweeping out per second is $s\,|\mathbf{v}_{21}|$, where $|\mathbf{v}_{21}|$ is the magnitude of $\mathbf{v}_2 - \mathbf{v}_1$. This is shown in Fig. 15-3. It is important to realize that the *magnitude* alone of $\mathbf{v}_{21}$ determines the collision volume. Whatever the angles of this vector, the volume $sv_{21}t$ will be the same.*

We wish to calculate the ensemble average of the volume an observer riding on particle 1 sees particle 2 sweep out during t seconds. Since s and t have nothing to do with the ensemble, it will be enough to find $\overline{v_{21}}$, where

$$v_{21} = |\mathbf{v}_{21}| = |\mathbf{v}_2 - \mathbf{v}_1|. \tag{15-2}$$

This average involves the velocity of both particle 1 and particle 2. If these velocities are uncorrelated, then

$$\overline{v_{21}} = \int d\mathbf{v}_1\, d\mathbf{v}_2 v_{21} \phi(\mathbf{v}_1)\phi(\mathbf{v}_2), \tag{15-3}$$

$$\overline{v_{21}} = \left(\frac{m}{2\pi kT}\right)^3 \int d\mathbf{v}_1\, d\mathbf{v}_2 v_{21} e^{-m(v_1{}^2 + v_2{}^2)/2kT}. \tag{15-4}$$

---

* This is so at least so long as particle 2 is not bouncing off some third particle. Such cases are neglected here. This procedure can be shown to be valid for gases at low density.

In order to perform the integration, it is necessary to change variables from v_1 and v_2 to

$$V_{21} = \tfrac{1}{2}(v_2 + v_1); \quad v_{21} = v_2 - v_1. \tag{15-5}$$

The variable V_{21} gives the velocity of the center of mass of the two particles. The change to *center of mass and relative velocity variables* given by Eq. 15-5 is very common in all kinds of studies relating to colliding particles. It is convenient because the center of mass motion V_{21} is undisturbed during the collision, and also because the product of the differentials is preserved:

$$dv_1 \, dv_2 = dV_{21} \, dv_{21}. \tag{15-6}$$

This can be checked by noting that the Jacobian of the transformation is unity for, say, the x component of the vectors:*

$$\frac{\partial(V_{21x}, v_{21x})}{\partial(v_{1x}, v_{2x})} = \begin{vmatrix} \dfrac{\partial V_{21x}}{\partial v_{1x}} & \dfrac{\partial v_{21x}}{\partial v_{1x}} \\[2ex] \dfrac{\partial V_{21x}}{\partial v_{2x}} & \dfrac{\partial v_{21x}}{\partial v_{2x}} \end{vmatrix} = \begin{vmatrix} \tfrac{1}{2} & -1 \\[1ex] \tfrac{1}{2} & 1 \end{vmatrix}$$

$$= \tfrac{1}{2} - (-\tfrac{1}{2}) = 1.$$

Since the same is true for the y and z components, Eq. 15-6 is verified. We also note that

$$v_1{}^2 + v_2{}^2 = 2V_{21}{}^2 + \tfrac{1}{2}v_{21}{}^2, \tag{15-7}$$

which may be checked immediately by the reader.

In center of mass and relative velocities, Eq. 15-4 becomes

$$\overline{v_{21}} = \left(\frac{m}{2\pi kT}\right)^3 \int dV_{21} \, dv_{21}v_{21}e^{-m(2V_{21}{}^2 + \tfrac{1}{2}v_{21}{}^2)/2kT}. \tag{15-8}$$

---

* The reader will recall from calculus that in changing from w and x as variables to $y(w, x)$ and $z(w, x)$ as variables, the products of differentials are related as follows:

$$dw \, dx = \frac{\partial(w, x)}{\partial(y, z)} \, dy \, dz,$$

where the so-called "Jacobian of the transformation" $\partial(w, x)/\partial(y, z)$ is given by the determinant

$$\frac{\partial(w, x)}{\partial(y, z)} = \begin{vmatrix} \dfrac{\partial w}{\partial y} & \dfrac{\partial x}{\partial y} \\[2ex] \dfrac{\partial w}{\partial z} & \dfrac{\partial x}{\partial z} \end{vmatrix}.$$

The integration over $d\mathbf{V}_{21}$ may be done directly to yield

$$\overline{v_{21}} = \left(\frac{m}{2\pi kT}\right)^3 \left(\frac{\pi kT}{m}\right)^{3/2} \int d\mathbf{v}_{21} v_{21} e^{-mv_{21}^2/4kT}. \tag{15-9}$$

In order to perform the integration over $d\mathbf{v}_{21}$, this three-dimensional volume element (in velocity space) may be put into spherical coordinates in a way completely analogous to Eq. 13-12.

$$d\mathbf{v}_{21} = v_{21}^2 \, dv_{21} \sin\theta \, d\theta \, d\chi. \tag{15-10}$$

Since there is no dependence in the integrand on either θ or χ, their integration gives 4π, as it did in the derivation of Eq. 14-8. The remaining integral is

$$\overline{v_{21}} = 4\pi \left(\frac{m}{2\pi kT}\right)^3 \left(\frac{\pi kT}{m}\right)^{3/2} \int_0^\infty dv_{21} v_{21}^3 e^{-mv_{21}^2/4kT}$$

$$= 4\pi \left(\frac{m}{2\pi kT}\right)^3 \left(\frac{\pi kT}{m}\right)^{3/2} \frac{1}{2} \left(\frac{4kT}{m}\right)^2$$

$$= 4\left(\frac{kT}{\pi m}\right)^{1/2} = \sqrt{2}\sqrt{8/\pi}\sqrt{kT/m},$$

$$\boxed{\overline{v_{21}} = \sqrt{2}\bar{v}.} \tag{15-11}$$

It is interesting that if one observes the speed of particle 2 in each member of the ensemble while sitting in the laboratory outside the box of gas, he then obtains an average speed $\bar{v}$. But if, in each member of the ensemble, one sits on top of some other molecule, say number 1, as it moves and notes the *apparent* speed of particle 2, the average of this apparent or relative speed is $\sqrt{2}$ times as large as $\bar{v}$.

COLLISION FREQUENCY AND MEAN FREE PATH

It is now possible to predict the frequency of collisions for a given particle. Not only does molecule 1 see molecule 2 sweeping out a collision volume of $\sqrt{2}s\bar{v}$ each second, but it also sees all the other particles in the box. The density of such particles is $(N-1)/V$, or $N(1 - 1/N)/V$. Certainly, $1/N$ may be neglected compared to 1.* So if particle 1 is sweeping out an average volume per second relative to other particles of

* Many times throughout this book, the quantity $N-1$ is replaced by N. Because N is so vast, this is an excellent approximation.

$\sqrt{2}s\bar{v}$, and if it sees N/V or ρ other particles per unit volume, one would expect it to collide with

$$Z_1 = \sqrt{2}s\rho\bar{v} = s\rho\left(\frac{16kT}{\pi m}\right)^{1/2} = 4s\rho\left(\frac{RT}{\pi M}\right)^{1/2} \tag{15-12}$$

other particles per second. The quantity Z_1 is called the **collision frequency for a particle.** The reader may quickly verify that for a gas like nitrogen at one atmosphere pressure and 25°C, if s is about 60 Å^2, Z_1 is about 10^{10} collisions per second.

With the rate of collisions of particle 1, Z_1, known, the average free path between collisions is easily found by realizing that a particle that travels an average distance of $\bar{v}$ per second and that collides an average of Z_1 times per second goes an average distance of

$$L = \frac{\bar{v}}{Z_1} = \frac{1}{\sqrt{2}s\rho} = \frac{kT}{\sqrt{2}sP} \tag{15-13}$$

between collisions. The quantity L is called the **mean free path.** It is inversely proportional to the particle density and (if s is truly independent of temperature) at constant density is independent of temperature. At constant temperature, it is inversely proportional to pressure. The mean free path, as calculated here, is a peculiar sort of average, difficult to define in terms of the ensemble, as the reader will see with a little thought. It does, however, afford an *idea* of what is going on in a gas. The reader will verify quickly that for nitrogen gas at one atmosphere pressure and 25°C, if s is about 60 Å^2, L is about 500 Å, some 100 times the radius of a molecule.

Another question easily answered at this point is the following: If molecule 1 is striking Z_1 particles per second on the average, what is the average number of collisions per second among *all* molecules contained in unit volume? Since the particle density is uniform, particle 1 has a probability of $1/V$ of being in the unit volume considered. However, we now are asking about collisions which may involve all N particles, not just particle 1. Thus the number of particles involved in collisions in the unit volume per second is N/V or ρ times Z_1. But *since each collision involves two particles*, the total number of collisions per unit volume per second Z is half this number:

$$Z = \tfrac{1}{2}\rho Z_1 = \frac{\sqrt{2}}{2} s\rho^2\bar{v} = 2s\rho^2\left(\frac{RT}{\pi M}\right)^{1/2}. \tag{15-14}$$

The reader may again verify quickly that in each cubic centimeter of the same hypothetical nitrogen gas mentioned above there are about 10^{29} collisions per second.

EFFUSION

One last simple problem will be solved here. Suppose there is a gas in a vessel which has a tiny hole in its side. Each gas molecule that hits the hole goes on out of the vessel. The rate of flow through the hole is small enough that the gas inside still is essentially at equilibrium, so the exponential distribution may be used. This process is called **molecular effusion.** It is slow enough to permit use of the equilibrium distribution only when the mean free path L of the particles is considerably greater than the dimensions of the hole. Otherwise there is a rush of gas through the hole which destroys the exponential distribution. The question is, how many molecules go out per unit area of hole per second?

The problem of finding the number of particles effusing through a hole of area A is essentially identical to that of Fig. 13-3 and Eq. 13-19. The only difference is that in Eq. 13-19 every collision of particle i with A is weighted by the change in momentum $2p_z$. In the case of effusion, on the other hand, the "collision" merely leads to the loss of one molecule through the hole. Therefore, the ensemble average giving the probability that particle i will effuse through unit area per second $P(i$ out$)$ is identical to Eq. 13-19 except for the replacement of $2p_z$ by unity:

$$P(i \text{ out}) = \frac{1}{At} \int_{-\infty}^{\infty} dp_x \int_{-\infty}^{\infty} dp_y \int_{-\infty}^{0} dp_z \int_{\tau} d\mathbf{r} f_1(\mathbf{r}, \mathbf{p}) \tag{15-15}$$

$$= \frac{1}{At} \int_{-\infty}^{\infty} dp_x \int_{-\infty}^{\infty} dp_y \int_{-\infty}^{0} dp_z \frac{\tau}{V} \left(\frac{\beta}{2\pi m}\right)^{3/2} e^{-\beta p^2/2m}$$

$$= \frac{1}{mV} \left(\frac{\beta}{2\pi m}\right)^{3/2} \int_{-\infty}^{\infty} dp_x \int_{-\infty}^{\infty} dp_y \int_{-\infty}^{0} dp_z \, |p_z| \, e^{-\beta(p_x^2 + p_y^2 + p_z^2)/2m}$$

$$\tag{15-16}$$

$$= \frac{1}{mV} \left(\frac{\beta}{2\pi m}\right)^{3/2} \pi^{1/2} \left(\frac{2m}{\beta}\right)^{1/2} \pi^{1/2} \left(\frac{2m}{\beta}\right)^{1/2} \frac{2m}{2\beta},$$

$$P(i \text{ out}) = \frac{1}{V} \left(\frac{kt}{2\pi m}\right)^{1/2} = \frac{At}{4V} \bar{v}. \tag{15-17}$$

The total number of particles effusing through unit area per unit time Γ_N is just N times $P(i$ out$)$:

$$\boxed{\Gamma_N = \frac{N\bar{v}}{4V} = \tfrac{1}{4}\rho\bar{v} = \rho\sqrt{kT/2\pi m} = \rho\sqrt{RT/2\pi M}.} \tag{15-18}$$

Obviously, gas will effuse in both directions through a hole. If the hole dimensions are small compared to a mean free path on both sides, the effusion occurs in both directions without interference. It is very unlikely that molecules would strike each other in the immediate vicinity of the hole. Eventually, if the gas on one side or the other is neither pumped off nor replenished, equilibrium will be reached.

PROBLEMS

15-1. At 25°C and 1 atm, if the total volume of a system containing ideal gas were considered as divided up into equal-sized cubes, one for each molecule, what would be the length of a cube? If the collision cross-section is 10 Å², what is the mean free path?

15-2. An excellent laboratory vacuum is 10^{-8} mm Hg. How many gas molecules are still contained in 1 mm³ (size of a pinhead) at 300°K? What is the mean free path if the collision cross-section is 15 Å²?

15-3. Prove that the number of collisions of gas molecules per unit area of wall per unit time in which the angle between the incoming direction of the particle and a normal to the surface is between θ and $\theta + d\theta$ is

$$\frac{N}{V}\left(\frac{2kT}{\pi m}\right)^{1/2} \sin\theta \cos\theta\, d\theta.$$

15-4. Find the number of collisions of gas molecules per unit area of wall per second in which the speed is between v and $v + dv$.

15-5. Calculate the root mean square velocity of the gas molecules effusing through a small hole. How does their average kinetic energy compare with that of the particles which do not effuse out? Why is this?

15-6. Two chambers are separated by a membrane, pierced with small holes. One chamber contains H_2, the other O_2. Both gases are at the same temperature. The pressure in the oxygen chamber is kept at twice that in the other. What happens?

15-7. How many molecules of N_2 effuse each minute through a square hole 0.01 mm on a side at 0.1 atm and 25°C?

15-8. During the time it would take a particle going $\bar{v}$ cm/sec to travel L cm, how many collisions would occur in a volume formed by A as base and L as height? Express the answer in terms of A and s.

15-9. Consider some arbitrary plane in the gas. Prove that the molecules on reaching that plane have, on the average, had their last collision at a distance $2L/3$ from the plane.

15-10. Compare Eqs. 15-12 and 15-18 and discuss.

16

CLASSICAL GAS—
EQUIPARTITION OF ENERGY

The only energy of an ideal gas considered so far is the translational kinetic energy of the molecules. This is of course only adequate completely to describe monatomic gases like helium and neon when they are unexcited electronically. Most gases of interest have the capacity for *internal* molecular energy contributions, as well as just kinetic energies. In this section the classical picture of these contributions is examined, because it is very useful pictorially and is identical to the quantum result in the high temperature limit. In Sec. 19 the problem is approached by using quantum mechanics.

Let each molecule in the ideal gas be made up of, say, n atoms. Thus, in order to determine completely the configuration of the molecule, $3n$ position coordinates must be fixed. The first three such coordinates are given when the center of mass of the molecule is located. Associated with each of these three coordinates classically is a kinetic energy of the form $p_x^2/2m$. In Eq. 13-13 and again in Prob. 13-4, it was shown that the ensemble average of the kinetic energy of a particle associated with *each* of the three classical coordinates of the center of mass is $\frac{1}{2}kT$.

If a molecule is *linear*, all the atoms lie in a straight line. Such a molecule is shown in Fig. 16-1. Specification of only two coordinates, angles of rotation about the x and y axes, completely orients the molecule. Associated with rotation about each of these two axes is a classical rotational energy $\frac{1}{2}I_x\omega_x^2$ or $\frac{1}{2}I_y\omega_y^2$, where the I's are the moments of inertia and the ω's are angular velocities about the axes noted. One might ask why the angle for rotation about the z axis need not be given and why there is not a third rotational energy $\frac{1}{2}I_z\omega_z^2$. Certainly, a purely classical treatment would contain this. Until the development of quantum mechanics, this was a real puzzle,* and we borrow the quantum result here. Quantum mechanics shows that the first energy level above zero for rotation about the z axis lies very high compared to kT. This means that the probability of excitation due to this cause, given by the Boltzmann factor, is negligible. Furthermore, any energy that is present in rotation about this axis is treated explicitly as electronic energy of the molecule

* For example, see Gibbs, p.x.

or as nuclear energy, depending on its origin. Therefore, the orientation of a linear molecule is given by two coordinates. Associated with each coordinate is a rotational energy $\frac{1}{2}I\omega^2$.

If the molecule is *non-linear*, it is necessary to specify three angles in order to orient it in space. In this case, there is a rotational energy of the form $\frac{1}{2}I\omega^2$ associated with rotation about each of the three axes.

Of the $3n$ total coordinates needed to fix a molecule in space, there are $3n - 5$ left to be specified for linear molecules, $3n - 6$ for non-linear. These coordinates are usually chosen as the so-called **normal coordinates**

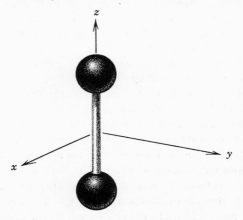

Fig. 16-1. Linear diatomic molecule shown aligned with the z axis.

of the molecule. Each of these $3n - 5$ or $3n - 6$ normal coordinates represents an independent vibrational motion in the molecule.

The example of a diatomic molecule helps clarify this. Since $n = 2$, only one normal coordinate need be found. It is known that the two atoms of a diatomic molecule are held together by a potential energy similar to that shown in Fig. 16-2 for hydrogen.

The two atoms vibrate back and forth in the potential well of Fig. 16-2. If the vibrational energy is not too great, say, up to half the energy required to dissociate the molecule, then the dotted parabola is not a bad approximation to the true potential. If the parabola is used for an interatomic potential, this is called the *harmonic approximation*. Classical particles vibrating in a parabolic potential well exhibit simple harmonic motion with total energy of the form $p^2/2\mu + Kq^2$. The p is a generalized momentum, μ a generalized or reduced mass, q a generalized coordinate, and K the force constant for the vibration. The first term gives the kinetic energy and the second the potential. There will be a contribution of this form for each of the $3n - 5$ or $3n - 6$ normal coordinates, so long as the harmonic approximation is made.

In summary, the total classical energy of a linear molecule may be written in the form

$$\epsilon = \frac{p_x{}^2}{2m} + \frac{p_y{}^2}{2m} + \frac{p_z{}^2}{2m} + \frac{I\omega_x{}^2}{2} + \frac{I\omega_y{}^2}{2}$$

$$+ \frac{p_1{}^2}{2\mu_1} + K_1 q_1{}^2 + \frac{p_2{}^2}{2\mu_2} + K_2 q_2{}^2 + \cdots. \tag{16-1}$$

The summation includes all the normal coordinates. For a non-linear molecule, the form of ϵ is similar. There is one more rotational contribution and one less pair of vibrational contributions.

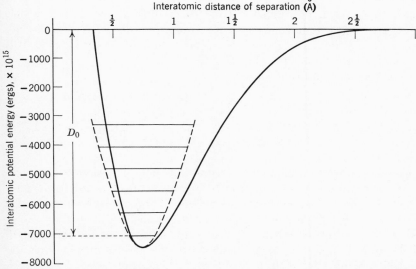

Fig. 16-2. Interatomic potential energy curve (solid line) for H_2 molecule. (From Hirschfelder, Curtiss, and Bird, p. 1058.)

We may choose the following as variables to describe a single polyatomic molecule: the position and momentum coordinates for the center of mass, the appropriate angles and angular momenta for the molecular orientation, and the normal coordinates q_i and associated momenta p_i for the orientation of the atoms relative to each other. To a first approximation, the energy of a molecule takes the form of a sum of squares of the variables (except for the positions and angles), as shown in Eq. 16-1. The variables appearing in the expression for ϵ may be written as x_i and the energy written

$$\epsilon = \sum_{i=1}^{\nu} a_i x_i{}^2. \tag{16-2}$$

The number of such terms in a linear polyatomic molecule is

$$\nu_{\text{linear}} = 5 + 2(3n - 5) = 6n - 5. \tag{16-3}$$

For a non-linear polyatomic molecule,

$$\nu_{\text{non-linear}} = 6 + 2(3n - 6) = 6n - 6. \tag{16-4}$$

For a monatomic molecule,

$$\nu_{\text{monatomic}} = 3. \tag{16-5}$$

In Eq. 13-13 and again in Prob. 13-4, the ensemble average of Eq. 16-2 was found for a monatomic gas. It was shown that each of the three terms in Eq. 16-2 contributed $\frac{1}{2}kT$ to the ensemble average of the particle energy $\bar{\epsilon}$. This was no coincidence, because *each of the ν terms* in the sum, Eq. 16-2, contributes $\frac{1}{2}kT$ to $\bar{\epsilon}$. The proof of this statement follows. It is a simple extension of Prob. 13-4.

The general expression for $\bar{\epsilon}$ is

$$\bar{\epsilon} = \frac{\int dx_1 \, dx_2 \cdots dx_\nu \left(\sum_{i=1}^{\nu} a_i x_i^2 \right) \exp\left(-\beta \sum_i a_i x_i^2 \right)}{\int dx_1 \, dx_2 \cdots dx_\nu \, \exp\left(-\beta \sum_i a_i x_i^2 \right)}. \tag{16-6}$$

One must know the limits on the various integrals. Translational momentum components of course go from $-\infty$ to $+\infty$, as do angular velocities. For vibrations, however, the limits on the p's and q's are less certain. It is enough to note that the integrand becomes vanishingly small for $p_i^2/2\mu_i$ or $K_i q_i^2$ much greater than kT, due to the damping of the exponential. Therefore, whatever the actual limits on the p's and q's may be, they too may be treated as $-\infty$ to $+\infty$ with negligible error.

The numerator of Eq. 16-6 consists of a sum of ν terms, each of which is of the form

$$\frac{\int_{-\infty}^{\infty} dx_1 \, dx_2 \cdots dx_\nu a_j x_j^2 \exp\left(-\beta \sum_i a_i x_i^2 \right)}{\int_{-\infty}^{\infty} dx_1 \, dx_2 \cdots dx_\nu \, \exp\left(-\beta \sum_i a_i x_i^2 \right)}. \tag{16-7}$$

All the integrals cancel between numerator and denominator of Eq. 16-7 except for that over dx_j:

$$\frac{\int_{-\infty}^{\infty} dx_j a_j x_j^2 e^{-\beta a_j x_j^2}}{\int_{-\infty}^{\infty} dx_j e^{-\beta a_j x_j^2}} = \frac{1}{2\beta} = \frac{1}{2}kT. \tag{16-8}$$

The values of the integrals are found in Appendix C. Each of the ν terms in Eq. 16-6 contributes $\frac{1}{2}kT$ to $\bar{\epsilon}$.

The following is a summary of what has been proved:

In classical mechanics, the ensemble average of the energy of a molecule is $\frac{1}{2}kT$ for each term in the expression for the energy with the form $a_j x_j^2$. There are three such terms for translational kinetic energy, one for rotation in each allowed direction and two for each normal mode of vibration. For linear polyatomic molecules, $\bar{\epsilon}$ is $(6n - 5)kT/2$; for non-linear polyatomic molecules, $\bar{\epsilon}$ is $(6n - 6)kT/2$; for monatomic molecules, $\bar{\epsilon}$ is $3kT/2$.

This general principle is called the **equipartition of energy.** The molar energies are just N_0 times the particle energies, or the same as above with R replacing k. The specific heats are the derivatives with respect to T, or the same as the energies with the T's omitted. The classical specific heat of a linear molecule is therefore greater than that of a non-linear molecule with the same number of atoms, since it has one more vibrational mode and one less rotational mode.

The question of when one would expect the classical results to be valid is treated in Secs. 18 and 19.

PROBLEMS

16-1. What molar specific heat would you expect under classical conditions for the following gases: (a) Ne, (b) O_2, (c) H_2O (non-linear), (d) CO_2 (linear), (e) $CHCl_3$?

16-2. Compare the average thermal energy of a particle, about kT, with the energy scales of Fig. 12-1 and Fig. 16-2. Let T be, say, $300°K$. Discuss the result.

17   QUANTUM GAS—PARTITION FUNCTION

In this section a general expression is found for the partition function of an ideal gas in terms of the quantum states of the molecules comprising it. Once this expression is evaluated, as is done in

Secs. 18 and 19, all the thermodynamic properties of ideal gas systems may be predicted by the methods of Sec. 11.

The first problem in determining the partition function

$$Q = \sum_{\substack{\text{all } N\text{-particle} \\ \text{quantum states}}} e^{-\beta E(\text{state})} \tag{17-1}$$

is finding what all the N-particle quantum states and their appropriate energies are. In an ideal gas there is no interaction between particles. Each particle is described quantum mechanically as if it were alone in the box. Thus, each particle is in one of the available *single-particle quantum states*. Associated with each of these, say, particle state i, is a particle energy ϵ_i.

The question is, what determines an N-particle state? Quantum mechanics gives the answer. The identical atoms and molecules that make up a gas (or a liquid) are indistinguishable from each other. Quantum mechanically this means that the state of a system is unchanged if two identical particles are interchanged. The property of particle indistinguishability must be reflected in the quantum mechanical representation of the system.* The conclusion is the following: *A quantum state for the N particles of an ideal gas is determined once the number of particles in each available particle state is given.* An N-particle state is *completely* specified by the so-called **occupation numbers,** that is, the numbers of particles occupying the various particle states. Absolutely no meaning may be attached to the question of which of a group of identical particles is in which state.

It is a general quantum mechanical conclusion that identical particles must be one or the other of two kinds. For the first kind, no two particles may be in the same particle state. The number of particles in any given particle state must be either 0 or 1. For the second kind, any number of particles may be in the same particle state. But interchange of such particles does not, of course, lead to a new state.

Experiments have shown that all particles whose spins† are odd multiples of $\frac{1}{2}$ are the first kind. Such particles are said to obey **Fermi-Dirac statistics** and are called **fermions.** Examples of such particles are electrons, protons, and neutrons. Similarly, all particles whose spins are even multiples of $\frac{1}{2}$ are the second kind. Such particles are said to obey **Bose-Einstein statistics** and are called **bosons.** Photons are examples of particles with integral spin. To determine the statistics which will be

---

* Best reference: Tolman, Sec. 76; others: Schiff, Sec. 32; Heitler, Chap. V; d'Abro, pp. 931–943.
† Heitler, Sec. 4; all general quantum mechanics references.

obeyed by an arbitrary molecule, ion, or atom, one may just add the spins of the fundamental particles comprising it. Thus, H, H_2, $(He^4)^{++}$, He^4, and D_2 are bosons and H^+, He^3, HD, and D are fermions. The unique properties substances possess because they are composed of either fermions or bosons are discussed in Secs. 22 to 25.

These ideas are illustrated by Table 17-1. The first column lists the various particle states, the number of which may very well be astronomical.

Table 17-1

Particle State i	Energy ϵ_i	Numbers of Particles, Example 1 N_i	Numbers of Particles, Example 2 N_i	Numbers of Particles, Example 3 N_i
. . .	. . .	. . .	. . .	. . .
. . .	. . .	. . .	. . .	. . .
11	ϵ_{11}	0	3	0
10	ϵ_{10}	1	1	1
9	ϵ_9	0	0	0
8	ϵ_8	0	2	0
7	ϵ_7	1	1	0
6	ϵ_6	0	2	0
5	ϵ_5	1	0	0
4	ϵ_4	1	3	1
3	ϵ_3	0	4	0
2	ϵ_2	1	1	0
1	ϵ_1	1	3	1
		Total = N	Total = N	Total = N

The second column gives the energies associated with the particle states. There may be some degenerate energies among these. That is, more than one of these ϵ's may have the same value. The things of importance are the different states, not the different energies. The last three columns give examples of distinct N-particle quantum states.

Each of the three examples in Table 17-1 gives the occupation numbers N_i of the various particle states, so each example specifies a different N-particle state. For a gas of fermions, examples 1 and 3 both could represent N-particle states, since these examples exhibit only the occupation number 0 or 1. For a gas of bosons, all three examples could represent available states, since there is no restriction on the numbers of bosons in a given particle state.

For convenience, the quantity q is defined as follows:

$$q = \sum_i e^{-\beta \epsilon_i}, \qquad (17\text{-}2)$$

where the sum is over all single-particle quantum states. The analogy between q and the partition function Q is apparent, and q is often called the **particle partition function.** The set of particle states over which the exponential is summed to give q is the complete set of states in the first column of Table 17-1. Our goal in this section is to express Q for an ideal gas in terms of q. The value of q is found in Secs. 18 and 19.

Consider the form of q^N. It is a product of N identical factors:

$$q^N = \left(\sum_i e^{-\beta \epsilon_i} \right) \left(\sum_j e^{-\beta \epsilon_j} \right) \cdots \left(\sum_l e^{-\beta \epsilon_l} \right), \qquad (17\text{-}3)$$

$$q^N = \sum_i \sum_j \cdots \sum_l e^{-\beta(\epsilon_i + \epsilon_j + \cdots + \epsilon_l)}. \qquad (17\text{-}4)$$

This has the form of a sum over states of the exponential in the energy of the N particles; thus it is *similar* to Q, Eq. 17-1. The question is, how does the set of states in q^N differ from the set in Q?

At this point, an example is useful. Suppose for the moment there were 11 particle states available and that N was 3. Then

$$q^N = \left(\sum_{i=1}^{11} e^{-\beta \epsilon_i} \right) \left(\sum_{j=1}^{11} e^{-\beta \epsilon_j} \right) \left(\sum_{k=1}^{11} e^{-\beta \epsilon_k} \right), \qquad (17\text{-}5)$$

$$q^N = e^{-\beta(\epsilon_1 + \epsilon_1 + \epsilon_1)} + e^{-\beta(\epsilon_1 + \epsilon_1 + \epsilon_2)} + e^{-\beta(\epsilon_1 + \epsilon_2 + \epsilon_1)}$$
$$+ e^{-\beta(\epsilon_2 + \epsilon_1 + \epsilon_1)} + e^{-\beta(\epsilon_1 + \epsilon_1 + \epsilon_3)} + \cdots. \qquad (17\text{-}6)$$

There would be 11^3 or 1331 terms in the expansion, Eq. 17-6. There is a separate term in q^N for *each* choice of the N indices $i, j, \ldots, l$. Choosing these indices not only determines the *numbers* of particles in each particle state, but it also determines *which* particles. There is a contribution in q^N for each different labeling of the different states occupied. In our example, consider the terms in q^N showing occupancy of particle states 1, 4, and 10:

$$e^{-\beta(\epsilon_1 + \epsilon_4 + \epsilon_{10})} + e^{-\beta(\epsilon_1 + \epsilon_{10} + \epsilon_4)} + e^{-\beta(\epsilon_4 + \epsilon_1 + \epsilon_{10})}$$
$$+ e^{-\beta(\epsilon_4 + \epsilon_{10} + \epsilon_1)} + e^{-\beta(\epsilon_{10} + \epsilon_1 + \epsilon_4)} + e^{-\beta(\epsilon_{10} + \epsilon_4 + \epsilon_1)}. \qquad (17\text{-}7)$$

This is precisely the condition of example 3 in Table 17-1. In Q there must be only one term showing occupancy of particle states 1, 4 and 10. In q^N there are six such terms. *Every* choice of three different particle states would be represented by one term in Q and by $3 \times 2 \times 1 = 3! = 6$ equal terms in q^N.

It is more difficult for cases in which each particle is not in a different particle state. For example, Eq. 17-6 shows that when only particle states 1 and 2 are occupied, there are three equal terms in q^N to represent this condition. When only particle state 1 is occupied, this condition is represented in q^N by just one term. In Q, on the other hand, the number of terms describing these cases depends on whether the system is composed of fermions or bosons. If the particles are fermions, then Q contains no terms of this nature. If the particles are bosons, then Q contains one term for each such case.

In summary: There are $N!$ equal terms in q^N for each term in Q which has all the N particles in different states. However, the terms in q^N in which two or more particles are in the same state are more complicated. They may be related to what should be in Q only by considering the effect of Fermi-Dirac or Bose-Einstein statistics.

This long discussion would be useless if it were not possible in many cases to ignore the complicating terms and write simply

$$Q \approx \frac{1}{N!} q^N. \tag{17-8}$$

This will be possible whenever the contribution to the value of q^N from terms with multiple occupancy of one or more states may be neglected compared to the contribution from terms having each particle in a different state.

Of great importance in determining what fraction of terms in q^N involve multiple occupancy is the ratio r of the number of particle states available to a particle to the number of particles in the system:

$$r \equiv \frac{\text{number of particle states with } \epsilon_i < kT}{N}. \tag{17-9}$$

It is assumed that a state is available to a particle if its energy, ϵ_i, is less than kT. In our example above, there are 11 states available to 3 particles, so r is 11/3. In the expansion of q^N, Eq. 17-6, the reader can verify that there are 11 terms representing triple occupancy of a single state, 330 terms representing double occupancy of one state with single occupancy of another, and the remaining 990 terms representing each of the three particles in a different state. Only $341/1331 = 0.256$ of the terms in q^N contribute to spoiling the equality of Eq. 17-8. If r were as large as 10, then the fraction of terms in q^N which spoil Eq. 17-8 becomes very small. An example is given in Prob. 17-1.

In the next section the value of r will be estimated, and it will be shown that for most gases of the sort one visualizes on hearing the word "gas," r is large enough that Eq. 17-8 is a very good approximation indeed.

Those few terms in q^N which show multiple occupancies may be ignored or handled in any way one sees fit. Since it is only how those terms are treated which establishes whether the gas obeys Fermi-Dirac or Bose-Einstein statistics, in the limit of large r, both fermions and bosons behave in the same way, that way being given by Eq. 17-8.

Systems for which r is much greater than unity, and thus for which Eq. 17-8 suffices to obtain Q, are said to be systems which "obey **Boltzmann statistics.**" Particles involved in a system "obeying Boltzmann statistics"

Fig. 17-1

may be either bosons or fermions. Their interchange does not lead to a new state. It is just that they are in systems for which r happens to be large enough to make Eq. 17-8 a useful approximation to Q:

$$Q_{\text{Boltzmann}} = \frac{1}{N!} q^N. \tag{17-10}$$

These distinctions may be seen clearly by considering a system containing only two particles.* Again consider the terms in q^N or q^2 as a function of the number of states available to a particle. If just two states are available, then q^2 contains four terms represented by the four squares in Fig. 17-1. If the particles are fermions, the only term which should appear in Q is $(1, 2)$, the upper right-hand corner (of course, the lower left-hand corner would be as good). If the particles are bosons, Q should contain not only the contribution from $(1, 2)$, but also contributions from the two shaded states on the diagonal. Clearly, r is not much greater then unity; in fact, it *is* unity in this example. There is a great difference between Q for fermions and for bosons in this case. Boltzmann statistics would add up the contributions from all four squares and divide the result by 2. That is, it would give half a contribution to each diagonal square. This is a compromise between the Fermi-Dirac and Bose-Einstein case.

However, things are different if ten states are available to the two particles, as shown in Fig. 17-2. In this case, Q for fermions would have contributions from all states above and to the right of the shaded ones.

* This pedagogical device was suggested to the author by Prof. J. E. Mayer.

For bosons, it would have those contributions plus the shaded ones. Boltzmann statistics would add half the contributions of the diagonal states as a compromise. As the number of states gets larger, clearly, the question of what is done with the shaded ones becomes immaterial.

Some authors say that a system described by Eq. 17-10 "obeys *corrected* Boltzmann statistics." The correction lies in the $1/N!$. For these authors,

	1	2	3	4	5	6	7	8	9	10
1	1,1	1,2	1,3	1,4	1,5	1,6	1,7	1,8	1,9	1,10
2	2,1	2,2	2,3	2,4	2,5	2,6	2,7	2,8	2,9	2,10
3	3,1	3,2	3,3	3,4	3,5	3,6	3,7	3,8	3,9	3,10
4	4,1	4,2	4,3	4,4	4,5	4,6	4,7	4,8	4,9	4,10
5	5,1	5,2	5,3	5,4	5,5	5,6	5,7	5,8	5,9	5,10
6	6,1	6,2	6,3	6,4	6,5	6,6	6,7	6,8	6,9	6,10
7	7,1	7,2	7,3	7,4	7,5	7,6	7,7	7,8	7,9	7,10
8	8,1	8,2	8,3	8,4	8,5	8,6	8,7	8,8	8,9	8,10
9	9,1	9,2	9,3	9,4	9,5	9,6	9,7	9,8	9,9	9,10
10	10,1	10,2	10,3	10,4	10,5	10,6	10,7	10,8	10,9	10,10

Fig. 17-2

a system for which q^N was used as the partition function would simply "obey Boltzmann statistics" or "obey classical Boltzmann statistics." The use of q^N for the partition function implies that each particle in the gas may in principle be given a label and followed as it moves around in the system. This changes the definition of a state for the N particles and changes the calculated values of the entropy, the free energies, and the chemical potential. It does not correspond to reality in a gas or liquid where the particles are free to migrate, but something analogous will be found in the case of crystals where each vibrational mode is different.

In the opinion of the author, when one uses q^N as the partition function, one should refer to his system as a gas of *non-identical* or *distinguishable* particles. When one uses $q^N/N!$, his gas is a "Boltzmann gas." The molecules are identical, but r of Eq. 17-9 is much greater than unity, so the difference between Bose-Einstein and Fermi-Dirac particles may be neglected. When r is not much larger than unity, then the question of whether the gas is composed of fermions or bosons becomes of vital importance. The reader of the statistical mechanical literature is warned in light of the above to pay close attention to the definitions used by each author.

PROBLEMS

17-1. Suppose that N is 3 and there are 30 particle states with energies less than kT. Thus, $r = 10$. What fraction of the terms in q^N exhibits multiple occupancy of a particle state?

17-2. Consider a two-particle system (two coins), with two particle states (head, tail) of equal energy available to each. If it was impossible to tell during a collision between the two coins whether they changed places or not, then the coins must be either fermions or bosons. If fermions, what two-particle states are allowed? What is the probability of one head and one tail? Of two heads? If bosons, what two-particle states are allowed? What is the probability of one head and one tail? Of two heads? If the coins are treated as distinguishable, what two-particle states are allowed? What is the probability of one head and one tail? Of two heads? If Boltzmann statistics were used to describe these coins, what would be the result? Would Boltzmann statistics be useful?

18   QUANTUM GAS—
TRANSLATIONAL ENERGY AND PRESSURE

This section uses quantum mechanics to study the translational part of the ideal gas partition function. It parallels the classical treatment given in Sec. 13. The ratio r of Sec. 17 is estimated, and the ensemble averages of the translational energy and the pressure are found.

In Sec. 17, the value of Q was related to the sum over states of a single particle,

$$q = \sum_i e^{-\beta \epsilon_i}, \tag{18-1}$$

where ϵ_i is the energy of a particle in particle state i. In general, this energy may be viewed as made up of two contributions, one from the translational kinetic energy of the center of mass of the particle, the other from the molecule's internal energy. The internal energy contains rotational, vibrational, electronic, and perhaps hybrid contributions. Specification of the state i is equivalent to giving *both* the translational *and* the internal state. The sum over *all* states may then be viewed as an independent summation over translational and internal states:

$$q = \sum_{\substack{\text{trans} \\ \text{states}}} \sum_{\substack{\text{int} \\ \text{states}}} e^{-\beta[\epsilon(\text{trans})+\epsilon(\text{int})]},$$

$$q = \left[\sum_{\substack{\text{trans} \\ \text{states}}} e^{-\beta\epsilon(\text{trans})} \right] \cdot \left[\sum_{\substack{\text{int} \\ \text{states}}} e^{-\beta\epsilon(\text{int})} \right], \tag{18-2}$$

$$q = q_{\text{trans}} \cdot q_{\text{int}}. \tag{18-3}$$

The notation q_{trans} and q_{int} is an obvious choice for the sums over all translational and internal states.

The ensemble averages of thermodynamic variables, Eqs. 11-13 to 11-21, are all found from the logarithm of Q. Since Q factorizes, $\ln Q$ becomes a sum:

$$\ln Q = \ln \left(\frac{1}{N!} q^N \right) = \ln \left(\frac{1}{N!} q_{\text{trans}}^N \cdot q_{\text{int}}^N \right),$$

$$\boxed{\ln Q = -\ln N! + N \ln q_{\text{trans}} + N \ln q_{\text{int}}.} \tag{18-4}$$

The first term in Eq. 18-4 arises from the indistinguishability of the particles. The second and third give the contributions to $\ln Q$ from translational and internal energies of the ideal gas molecules.

In this section, attention is given only to the translational contribution. It is necessary to know the set of allowed translational states for a free particle in a box of volume V and their corresponding energy levels. These are obtained by solving the Schrödinger equation,

$$\nabla^2 \psi = -\frac{2m\epsilon_{\text{trans}}}{\hbar^2} \psi, \tag{18-5}$$

with appropriate boundary conditions ($\psi = 0$ at walls of box).* The

---

* Almost all books on quantum mechanics, physical chemistry, intermediate physics, or statistical mechanics solve this problem. In particular, see Eisberg, Sec. 8-5; Pauling and Wilson, Sec. 14; Barrow, Chap. 1.

following symbols appear in Eq. 18-5: m is the mass of the particle; $\hbar$ is $h/2\pi$, where h is Planck's constant, $\hbar = 1.054 \times 10^{-27}$ erg-sec; ψ is the so-called *wave function*, a function of position $\mathbf{r}$.

The wave function can satisfy Eq. 18-5 *and* be zero at the walls only for certain discrete translational states and corresponding energies:

$$\epsilon_{\text{trans}}(n_x, n_y, n_z) = \frac{\pi^2 \hbar^2}{2ma^2}(n_x^2 + n_y^2 + n_z^2);$$ (18-6)

n_x, n_y, n_z positive integers greater than 0;
different quantum state for each choice of n_x, n_y, and n_z.

For convenience, the box has been chosen as a cube of length a. Boxes with other shapes introduce no important new features. A *state* is specified

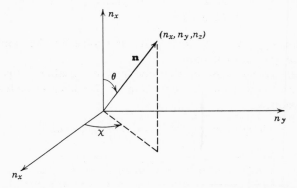

Fig. 18-1. Choice of n_x, n_y, n_z visualized as a point in three-dimensional quantum number space.

by choice of the three positive integers n_x, n_y, and n_z, which may take any value greater than zero. Equation 18-6 may be viewed as giving the translational energy of a particle as the sum of three terms, one for translation in the x direction, one in the y direction, and one in the z direction. The n's are called **translational quantum numbers.**

From time to time it will prove convenient to visualize each choice of n_x, n_y, and n_z as a *point* in the positive octant of a three-dimensional quantum number space, illustrated in Fig. 18-1. Each point in this space may also be described by a vector $\mathbf{n}$ with components n_x, n_y, n_z. Equation 18-6 shows that ϵ_{trans} depends only on the magnitude of the vector $\mathbf{n}$.

The first use to which Eq. 18-6 will be put is to calculate the contribution from translational states to the ratio r of Eq. 17-9. A translational state will be counted for every point in the quantum number space which leads to an energy $\epsilon_{\text{trans}} < kT$. The maximum value that n^2 may have is easily found by equating the maximum translational energy to kT:

$$\frac{\pi^2 \hbar^2 n_{max}^2}{2ma^2} = kT, \tag{18-7}$$

$$n_{max} = \sqrt{\frac{2MkT}{N_0}} \, \frac{a}{\pi\hbar}. \tag{18-8}$$

The question is, how many points in the space of Fig. 18-1 lie within a distance n_{max} of the origin? It is possible to estimate the answer by simply *associating with each point* in quantum number space a *volume*, one quantum number on a side. Then, the number of points within a distance n_{max} of the origin is approximately equal to the volume of an eighth of a sphere of radius n_{max}. This volume divided by N is the desired ratio:

$$r = \frac{1}{N} \cdot \frac{1}{8} \cdot \frac{4}{3} \pi n_{max}^3, \tag{18-9}$$

$$r = \frac{\pi}{6N} \left(\frac{2MkT}{N_0}\right)^{3/2} \frac{V}{\pi^3 \hbar^3}. \tag{18-10}$$

This may be simplified by using the ideal gas law. It is desired to express the pressure in atmospheres, and one atmosphere is approximately 10^6 dynes/cm².

$$r = \left(\frac{2MkT}{N_0}\right)^{3/2} \frac{kT}{10^6 \cdot 6\pi^2 P \hbar^3},$$

$$\boxed{r = \frac{M^{3/2} T^{5/2}}{50P}.} \tag{18-11}$$

In Eq. 18-11, P is in atmospheres.

Whenever Eq. 8-11 is much greater than unity, there are enough available translational states alone to make the use of Boltzmann statistics satisfactory. Even for so light a gas as hydrogen at one atmosphere pressure and only 20°K, Eq. 18-11 gives a value of over 50 for r. Furthermore, Eq. 18-11 neglects possible rotational states below kT in energy for polyatomic molecules. Thus, for most gases of the kind we are used to dealing with, r is large enough that Boltzmann statistics give an excellent description of the system.

The next use to which Eq. 18-6 will be put is to calculate q_{trans}, enabling us to find the translational contribution to all the thermodynamic variables through the equations of Sec. 11.

It is notationally convenient to define what might be called the **characteristic temperature of translation**, Θ_{trans}:

$$k\Theta_{trans} \equiv \frac{\pi^2 \hbar^2}{2ma^2}. \tag{18-12}$$

In terms of Θ_{trans}, q_{trans} is simply

$$q_{\text{trans}} = \sum_{\substack{\text{trans} \\ \text{states}}} e^{-\epsilon_{\text{trans}}/kT},$$

$$q_{\text{trans}} = \sum_{n_x=1}^{\infty} \sum_{n_y=1}^{\infty} \sum_{n_z=1}^{\infty} e^{-\Theta_{\text{trans}}(n_x{}^2 + n_y{}^2 + n_z{}^2)/T}, \tag{18-13}$$

$$= \left(\sum_{n_x=1}^{\infty} e^{-n_x{}^2 \Theta_{\text{trans}}/T} \right) \left(\sum_{n_y=1}^{\infty} e^{-n_y{}^2 \Theta_{\text{trans}}/T} \right) \left(\sum_{n_z=1}^{\infty} e^{-n_z{}^2 \Theta_{\text{trans}}/T} \right),$$

$$q_{\text{trans}} = \left(\sum_{n=1}^{\infty} e^{-n^2 \Theta_{\text{trans}}/T} \right)^3. \tag{18-14}$$

The quantities in the three parentheses above differ only in the name given to the dummy summation index, so they are identical.

Each term in the sum in Eq. 18-14 may be plotted as a dot against n, as in Fig. 18-2a. The complete sum may be viewed, then, as the sum of the

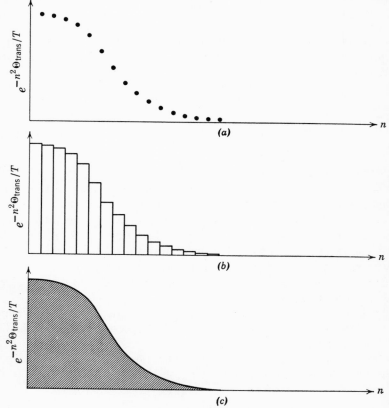

Fig. 18-2. Plots of $e^{-n^2 \Theta_{\text{trans}}/T}$ versus n.

areas of an infinite number of strips, one unit wide and $e^{-n^2\Theta_{\text{trans}}/T}$ units high, as shown in Fig. 18-2b. The total area of all the strips could be found accurately simply by integrating the continuous function $e^{-n^2\Theta_{\text{trans}}/T}$ over dn if the number of cases in which the height of a strip changed markedly in passing from one value of n to the next was negligible. The reader may quickly verify that this will be true whenever $\Theta_{\text{trans}}/T \ll 1$. This inequality is the same as

$$MTa^2 \gg 2.4 \times 10^{-14} \text{ g-cm}^2\text{-deg/mole}. \tag{8-15}$$

The left-hand side of Eq. 18-15 is 0.2 for hydrogen gas at 10°K in a box one millimeter on a side. Therefore, one is more than justified in integrating to get the value of the sum, as illustrated in Fig. 18-2c. In fact, Figs. 18-2 vastly exaggerate the effect in the exponential on changing the value of n by one unit. Finding the value of the sum by integrating is equivalent to what is known in calculus as taking the first term of an *Euler-Maclaurin expansion* of the sum.*

$$q_{\text{trans}} = \left(\int_0^\infty dn\, e^{-n^2\Theta_{\text{trans}}/T} \right)^3 \tag{18-16}$$

$$= \left(\frac{\pi^{1/2}T^{1/2}}{2\Theta_{\text{trans}}^{1/2}} \right)^3,$$

$$\boxed{q_{\text{trans}} = V\left(\frac{mkT}{2\pi\hbar^2} \right)^{3/2}.} \tag{18-17}$$

Knowing q_{trans}, it is easy to find $\bar{\epsilon}_{\text{trans}}$ and $\bar{E}_{\text{trans}}$ by using Eqs. 18-4 and 11-10:

$$\bar{\epsilon}_{\text{trans}} = kT^2 \left(\frac{\partial \ln q_{\text{trans}}}{\partial T} \right)_{V,N_i}$$

$$= kT^2 \left(\frac{\partial \ln T^{3/2}}{\partial T} \right)_{V,N_i},$$

$$\boxed{\bar{\epsilon}_{\text{trans}} = \tfrac{3}{2}kT.} \tag{18-18}$$

$$\bar{E}_{\text{trans}} = kT^2 \left(\frac{\partial \ln Q_{\text{trans}}}{\partial T} \right)_{V,N_i}$$

$$= N\bar{\epsilon}_{\text{trans}},$$

$$\boxed{\bar{E}_{\text{trans}} = \tfrac{3}{2}NkT.} \tag{18-19}$$

* Proved in most calculus books, given in Mayer and Mayer, p. 431.

It is no surprise that these results are the same as those obtained through using classical mechanics, Eqs. 13-13 and 13-14. The summation over translational quantum numbers is the same as integration over momenta, so the results had to be identical.

It is also interesting to find the pressure of an ideal gas through the quantum mechanical partition function. Equation 11-18 shows $\bar{P}$ to be

$$\bar{P} = kT\left(\frac{\partial \ln Q}{\partial V}\right)_{T,N_i}. \tag{18-20}$$

Of the three terms in Eq. 18-4 which comprise $\ln Q$, the only one which depends on the volume V is $N \ln q_{\text{trans}}$. The *internal* molecular states and energy levels do not depend on the volume. Therefore, the ensemble average of the pressure of an ideal gas is simply

$$\bar{P} = NkT\left(\frac{\partial \ln q_{\text{trans}}}{\partial V}\right)_{T,N_i} \tag{18-21}$$

$$= NkT\left(\frac{\partial \ln V}{\partial V}\right)_{T,N_i};$$

$$\boxed{\bar{P}V = NkT.} \tag{18-22}$$

The result for the translational energy and pressure of an ideal Boltzmann gas is the same if we use quantum mechanics as it is if we use classical mechanics. The method of finding q_{trans} in this section is typical of methods often used to handle other quantum problems in statistical mechanics. Conceptually, the quantum problems are probably less difficult than the classical ones. However, the summations over discrete quantum numbers are sometimes harder to evaluate than integrations would be. Turning the summations into integrals as was done here is often practicable.

In general, though, it is the *difference* between the result found by summing over discrete quantum numbers and the result found by integrating which contains all the explicit *quantum* effects. Whenever conditions are such that integration correctly gives the value of the sum, the result is the same as that which.would have arisen from a strictly classical approach to the problem. This is the so-called **classical limit** of the quantum problem.

The amount of energy needed to go from one translational level to the next higher one might be called the value of a **quantum of translational energy.** It is roughly of the order of $k\Theta_{\text{trans}}$. As noted above, the classical limit arose because a quantum of translational energy is much, much less than kT, even for very low temperatures. It will be seen in the next section that this result is general. Whenever a quantum of energy contributing to ϵ is much less than kT, that contribution behaves classically.

PROBLEMS

18-1. Find q_{trans} from Eq. 18-13, integrating in spherical coordinates instead of in Cartesian coordinates.

18-2. What is the ratio of populations of helium atoms in translational state $n_x = n_y = n_z = 1$ to helium atoms in translational state $n_x = n_y = 1$, $n_z = 2$? The temperature is $200°K$; the volume is a cube 10 cm on an edge.

18-3. Using Eq. 18-4 and the value of q_{trans}, what is the translational contribution to the entropy? To the chemical potential?

18-4. Verify Eq. 18-15.

18-5. Estimate the temperature below which Boltzmann statistics would begin to fail for helium gas at one atmosphere pressure.

18-6. The energy levels of Eq. 18-6 are correct for a cubical box. If, however, the box is a rectangular parallelepiped of dimensions $a \times b \times c$, the levels are given by

$$\epsilon_{trans}(n_x, n_y, n_z) = \frac{\pi^2 \hbar^2}{2m}\left(\frac{n_x^2}{a^2} + \frac{n_y^2}{b^2} + \frac{n_z^2}{c^2}\right).$$

Prove that q_{trans} as given by Eq. 18-17 is unchanged for the rectangular box.

18-7. Verify Eq. 18-6 by solving the Schrödinger equation. Any of the references mentioned will give considerable help.

19

QUANTUM GAS—
INTERNAL MOLECULAR ENERGIES

In Sec. 18, translational energy was studied. This section considers the contribution made by the internal molecular energies to the partition function of an ideal gas, that is, the last term of Eq. 18-4. This section treats only rotational, vibrational, and electronic contributions in the approximation that these are independent and additive:

$$\epsilon = \epsilon_{trans} + \epsilon_{int}, \tag{19-1}$$

$$\epsilon = \epsilon_{trans} + \epsilon_{rot} + \epsilon_{vib} + \epsilon_{elect}; \tag{19-2}$$

$$q = q_{trans} \cdot q_{int}, \tag{19-3}$$

$$q = q_{trans} \cdot q_{rot} \cdot q_{vib} \cdot q_{elect}. \tag{19-4}$$

The q's have the customary meaning of being the sums over all appropriate states of the proper exponentials. The equation analogous to Eq. 18-4 is

$$\ln Q = -\ln N! + N \ln q_{\text{trans}} + N \ln q_{\text{rot}} \atop + N \ln q_{\text{vib}} + N \ln q_{\text{elect}}.$$ (19-5)

ROTATION

Solution of the Schrödinger equation for the states and energies of a linear, rigid rotator yields* a set of states which have the following energies:

$$\epsilon_{\text{rot}}(j) = \frac{\hbar^2}{2I} j(j + 1);$$ (19-6)

j may be 0, 1, 2, 3, . . . ,
each level has degeneracy of $2j + 1$.

The quantity I is the moment of inertia about the center of mass and j is the **rotational quantum number,** which may have value 0, 1, 2, 3, ... Each rotational state is characterized by two quantum numbers, j and m_j. There are $2j + 1$ possible values of m_j for each value of j. Choice of m_j does not affect the energy of the state. That is, the *degeneracy* of $\epsilon_{\text{rot}}(j)$, given by Eq. 19-6, is $2j + 1$. Moments of inertia of molecules may be calculated from their known structure.

The rotational quantum of energy is of the order of $\hbar^2/2I$, and it usually is less than kT. A convenient way to tabulate rotational data about different molecules is through the **characteristic temperature of rotation** Θ_{rot}, analogous to Θ_{trans} of Eq. 18-12:

$$k\Theta_{\text{rot}} = \frac{\hbar^2}{2I}.$$ (19-7)

Values of Θ_{rot} for some common gases are given in Table 19-1.

For most gases except hydrogen, the rotational energy gives its classical contribution down to the temperature of liquefaction. Since hydrogen is so light, its small moment of inertia makes it exceptional. For temperatures much below 85°K, $e^{-\epsilon_{\text{rot}}/kT}$ will be very small for $j \neq 0$, so almost all the hydrogen molecules will have $j = 0$, and therefore, from Eq. 19-6,

* The quantum mechanics references treat this, but it is difficult. A simple, intuitive treatment is given by Barrow, Chap. 3.

zero rotational energy. Up to approximately Θ_{rot}, $\bar{\epsilon}_{rot}$ stays very small. It then rises rapidly as a function of temperature to reach the classical value.

We shall now calculate the classical limit of q_{rot}, which will yield not only $\bar{\epsilon}_{rot}$ but also the rotational contributions to the various thermodynamic variables:

$$q_{rot} = \sum_{\substack{rot \\ states}} e^{-\epsilon(rot)/kT} = \sum_{\substack{rot \\ states}} e^{-j(j+1)\Theta_{rot}/T}. \tag{19-8}$$

Naturally, the question arises, what is a rotational state? We are treating only linear molecules, of which there are only two kinds: those that are

Table 19-1. Parameters for Common Diatomic Molecules

	Θ_{rot}, °K	Θ_{vib}, °K	D_0, ergs $\times 10^{15}$
H_2	85.4	6,210	7,140
HCl	15.2	4,140	7,090
HBr	12.1	3,700	5,770
HI	9.0	3,200	4,410
N_2	2.86	3,340	11,820
CO	2.77	3,070	14,640
NO	2.42	2,690	8,480
O_2	2.07	2,230	8,140
Cl_2	0.346	810	3,970
Br_2	0.116	470	3,160
I_2	0.054	310	2,470

Based on a table in Hill, p. 153.

symmetric about the center and those that are not. *Asymmetric* linear molecules may have *any* value of j. *Symmetric* linear molecules (in a given nuclear state) may have either any *odd* value of j or any *even* value of j. Every value of j, however, has its degeneracy of $2j + 1$.

Treating this complication is easy in the classical limit. Since adjacent values of j make virtually identical contributions to q_{rot}, counting only half the states leads to just half as big a value for q_{rot} as would be found if they were all counted. We find q_{rot} by first counting all values of j. Then if the molecule is symmetric, this result is divided by 2; if asymmetric, the result is divided by unity. We note this alternative by dividing by the so-called **symmetry number** σ; $\sigma = 1$ for an asymmetric molecule,

$\sigma = 2$ for a symmetric molecule:*

$$q_{rot} = \frac{1}{\sigma} \sum_{j=0}^{\infty} (2j + 1)e^{-j(j+1)\Theta_{rot}/T}.$$ (19-9)

In the classical limit this becomes

$$q_{rot} = \frac{1}{\sigma} \int_0^{\infty} dj(2j + 1)e^{-j(j+1)\Theta_{rot}/T}.$$ (19-10)

This integration is easily done by making the following change of variable:

$$j(j + 1) = z, \quad (2j + 1)\, dj = dz;$$ (19-11)

$$q_{rot} = \frac{1}{\sigma} \int_0^{\infty} dz\, e^{-z\Theta_{rot}/T},$$ (19-12)

$$\boxed{q_{rot} = \frac{T}{\sigma\Theta_{rot}} = \frac{2IkT}{\sigma\hbar^2}.}$$ (19-13)

From Eq. 19-13 it is easy to determine that the classical limit of $\bar{\epsilon}_{rot}$ for linear molecules is

$$\bar{\epsilon}_{rot} = kT^2\left(\frac{\partial \ln q_{rot}}{\partial T}\right)_{V,N_i},$$ (19-14)

$$\boxed{\bar{\epsilon}_{rot} = kT,}$$ (19-15)

which of course agrees with the value found classically in Sec. 16.

In Fig. 19-1, the rotational contributions to the molar energy and heat capacity of an ideal diatomic gas are plotted as functions of temperature. The rotational contribution to the energy, as shown in Fig. 19-1a, starts off very small for $T \ll \Theta_{rot}$. The energy to excite molecules rotationally must come from collisions between molecules in the gas. At these low temperatures, colliding molecules usually have so little kinetic energy that it is impossible for collisions to furnish a whole quantum of rotational energy. Therefore, most molecules remain rotationally unexcited. One might say the rotational energy is "frozen out." As the temperature increases toward Θ_{rot}, more of the molecular collisions are energetic enough to leave one or more of the colliding particles rotationally excited. Thus, $\bar{E}_{rot}$ gradually increases until it approaches its classical value of RT. The rotational degrees of freedom are "thawed out" at temperatures above Θ_{rot}.

* Further discussed in Sec. 31. Extensively discussed by Mayer and Mayer, Sec. 7,b.

The slope of the energy curve is the rotational contribution to the specific heat. Because at low temperatures almost no energy is present in rotational contributions, $\overline{C}_{V,\,\text{rot}}$ is very small. Then, as the rotational degrees of freedom thaw out and the molecules begin to rotate, $\overline{C}_{V,\text{rot}}$

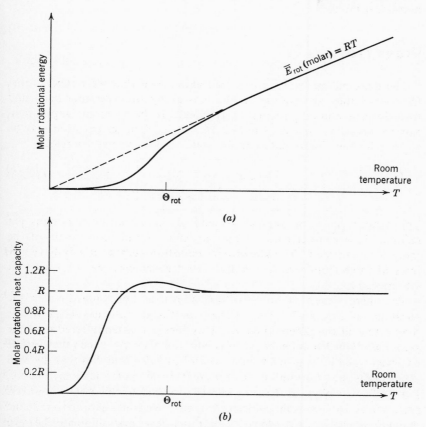

Fig. 19-1. Rotational contributions to (*a*) molar energy and (*b*) molar heat capacity of ideal diatomic gas as function of temperature.

increases. It must go through a maximum as $\overline{E}_{\text{rot}}$ hurries to catch up with RT. Then $\overline{C}_{V,\,\text{rot}}$ slowly approaches its asymptotic value R.

The value of q_{rot}, Eq. 19-13, will be used in Sec. 20 in finding the other thermodynamic variables. Non-linear molecules are not treated in this section. Their rotational partition function in the classical limit* is an

---

* Mayer and Mayer, pp. 191–199.

intuitive extension of Eq. 19-13:

$$q_{rot} = \frac{\pi^{1/2}}{\sigma}\left(\frac{2I_x kT}{\hbar^2}\right)^{1/2}\left(\frac{2I_y kT}{\hbar^2}\right)^{1/2}\left(\frac{2I_z kT}{\hbar^2}\right)^{1/2}, \tag{19-16}$$

where I_x, I_y, and I_z are the three principal moments of inertia of the non-linear molecule.

VIBRATION

The diatomic molecules are treated above as if they were rigid rotors. Of course, they are not rigid; the two atoms are vibrating back and forth in their mutual potential energy field. If the harmonic approximation to this field is made, as in Sec. 16, the Schrödinger equation may be solved* for the vibrational quantum states and associated energies:

$$\boxed{\epsilon_{vib}(n) = (n + \tfrac{1}{2})\hbar\omega; \tag{19-17}}$$

n may be 0, 1, 2, 3, . . . ,
no degeneracy arises from vibration.

The quantity ω is the angular velocity of the vibration in radians per second. It is characteristic of the particular normal coordinate of the molecule concerned. The **vibrational quantum number** n may have any integral value from zero to infinity. No degeneracies are introduced by vibrational levels.

The energy levels of Eq. 19-17 are shown as horizontal lines in the parabola of Fig. 16-2. The lowest vibrational state lies $\hbar\omega/2$ above the bottom of the potential curve. This energy is often referred to as the **zero point vibrational energy.** It is vibrational energy which the particle has even when in its ground state. Use of Eq. 19-17 implies that the zero of energy is the "bottom" or lowest point on the potential energy curve, Fig. 16-2. No physical meaning can be attached to this point, however, since $\hbar\omega/2$ is as low as the molecule can get. We could choose to redefine the zero of energy as the lowest vibrational level and eliminate the zero point energies from consideration. We choose, however, to retain them.

In Table 19-1 vibrational data are tabulated for common molecules in terms of the **characteristic temperature of vibration** Θ_{vib}:

$$k\Theta_{vib} = \hbar\omega. \tag{19-18}$$

Also given in Table 19-1 are values of the depth of the potential wells D_0, from the energy of separation (the zero of Fig. 16-2) to the lowest vibrational level.

* All quantum mechanics books treat this. See Barrow, Chap. 2; Pauling and Wilson, Sec. 11; Eisberg, Sec. 8-6.

Because of the large values of Θ_{vib} compared to room temperatures, most gas molecules are vibrationally unexcited. The quantum of vibrational energy, $\hbar\omega$, is large compared to kT. This is convenient, because use of the harmonic potential approximation to the real potential curve, Fig. 16-2, is poor for energies higher than about $D_0/2$. So few molecules have this much vibrational energy at reasonable temperatures that this difficulty may usually be neglected.

On the other hand, it is of course unreasonable to integrate to find q_{vib}:

$$q_{vib} = \sum_{n=0}^{\infty} e^{-(n+\frac{1}{2})\Theta_{vib}/T}, \tag{19-19}$$

$$q_{vib} = e^{-\Theta_{vib}/2T} \sum_{n=0}^{\infty} (e^{-\Theta_{vib}/T})^n. \tag{19-20}$$

The rewriting in Eq. 19-20 suggests a way to sum the series. It is well known that*

$$\sum_{n=0}^{\infty} a^n = \frac{1}{1-a}, \tag{19-21}$$

so Eq. 19-20 is simply

$$q_{vib} = \frac{e^{-\Theta_{vib}/2T}}{1 - e^{-\Theta_{vib}/T}} \cdot \tag{19-22}$$

The numerator of Eq. 19-22 represents the zero point energy. The exponential in the denominator represents the contribution of vibrationally excited molecules.

Knowing q_{vib}, it is easy to find $\bar{\epsilon}_{vib}$:

$$\bar{\epsilon}_{vib} = kT^2 \left(\frac{\partial \ln q_{vib}}{\partial T} \right)_{V,N_i}$$

$$= \frac{k\Theta_{vib}}{2} + \frac{k\Theta_{vib}e^{-\Theta_{vib}/T}}{1 - e^{-\Theta_{vib}/T}},$$

$$\bar{\epsilon}_{vib} = \frac{k\Theta_{vib}}{2} + \frac{k\Theta_{vib}}{e^{\Theta_{vib}/T} - 1} \cdot \tag{19-23}$$

* The reader may both verify and remember this by rederiving it:

$$1 - a \overline{\left)\begin{array}{l} 1 + a + a^2 + a^3 + \cdots \\ \overline{1} \\ \underline{1 - a} \\ a \\ \underline{a - a^2} \\ a^2 \cdots \end{array}\right.}$$

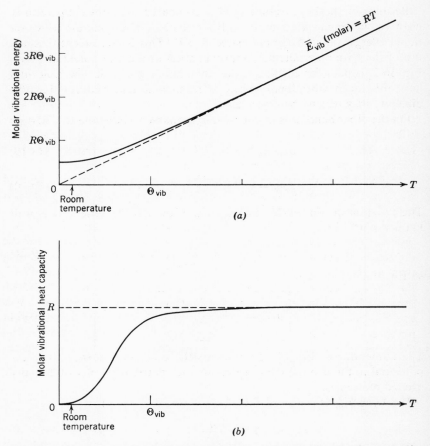

Fig. 19-2. Vibrational contributions to (a) molar energy and (b) molar heat capacity of ideal diatomic gas as function of temperature.

The first term in Eq. 19-23 is the zero point energy. It arises because the zero of energy used in Eq. 19-23 is the *bottom* of the potential well of Fig. 16-2. If the energy zero were chosen as that of infinite separation of the particles, then

$$\bar{\epsilon}_{vib} = \frac{k\Theta_{vib}}{e^{\Theta_{vib}/T} - 1} - D_0. \qquad (19\text{-}24)$$

This choice of zero is often used, especially in problems involving chemical reactions, as in Sec. 30.

The vibrational contribution to the system energy is simply

$$\bar{E}_{vib} = N\bar{\epsilon}_{vib}. \qquad (19\text{-}25)$$

The vibrational heat capacity is

$$\overline{C_{V,\text{vib}}} = N\left(\frac{\partial \bar{\epsilon}_{\text{vib}}}{\partial T}\right)_{V,N_i},$$

$$\overline{C_{V,\text{vib}}} = \frac{Nk\Theta_{\text{vib}}^2 e^{\Theta_{\text{vib}}/T}}{T^2(e^{\Theta_{\text{vib}}/T} - 1)^2}. \tag{19-26}$$

In Fig. 19-2, the vibrational contributions to the molar energy and heat capacity of an ideal diatomic gas are plotted as functions of temperature. Vibrational modes thaw out over a relatively much greater temperature range than rotational modes. Also, there is no hump in the specific heat curve, because $\bar{E}_{\text{vib}}$ starts above its asymptotic line at $T = 0$.

In Prob. 19-8, the reader will verify that the high temperature limit of $\bar{\epsilon}_{\text{vib}}$ is kT, the classical limit for each vibrational mode of energy. This is just what was found in Sec. 16.

For polyatomic molecules containing n particles, the $3n - 5$ or $3n - 6$ different *normal coordinates* mentioned in Sec. 16 must be found for the molecule. The total vibrational energy may then be viewed as coming from a sum of $3n - 5$ or $3n - 6$ contributions of the form of Eq. 19-17. Each normal coordinate has its own characteristic frequency ω, although several ω's may be the same. That is, there may be degeneracies. It is generally no easy job to analyze a molecule to determine how its complicated vibrational motions may be so simply viewed and then to find the normal frequencies ω.* Each normal coordinate contributes its factor to q_{vib} in the form of Eq. 19-22.

ELECTRONIC

Solution of the Schrödinger equation for the *electronic* states and energies of the molecule may be done in principle. This information is also obtainable from spectroscopic experiments. For most molecules commonly treated, the excited electronic levels lie so far above the ground state compared to kT that all the molecules may be considered to be in the ground state. The electronic partition function is simply the degeneracy of the electronic ground state g_0:

$$q_{\text{elect}} = \sum_{\substack{\text{elect} \\ \text{states}}} e^{-\beta\epsilon(\text{state})}$$

$$= \sum_{\substack{\text{states of} \\ \text{zero energy}}} e^0,$$

$$\boxed{q_{\text{elect}} = g_0.} \tag{19-27}$$

* Barrow, Chap. 6; Davidson, pp. 178–194.

With temperatures for which kT is much less than the energy required to excite a molecule electronically, the electronic contribution to the energy is merely the ground state energy. This may be set equal to zero. In this situation the electronic heat capacity is zero.

The Cl atom, for example, has a ground state energy level with degeneracy of 4. Thus q_{elect} for a gas of Cl atoms is 4, and the electronic contribution to $\ln Q$ is $N \ln 4$. This adds $Nk \ln 4$ to the entropy of the system, though it does not change the energy or heat capacity.

The NO molecule is one for which the amount ϵ by which the first excited state lies above the ground state is only $(178 \deg)k$. Both the ground state and the first excited states are doubly degenerate, so q_{elect} is $2 + 2e^{-\epsilon/kT}$ for NO. In Prob. 20-1 the effects of such a situation are computed.

SUMMARY

In review, finding average molecular energies is surprisingly simple, conceptually. We find a pattern which occurs over and over. When the quantum levels for a given contribution to $\bar{\epsilon}$ are widely spaced with respect to kT, most molecules are in the lowest level. The contribution to the specific heat at such low temperatures is negligible. As the temperature is raised, the various contributions thaw out. At even the very lowest temperatures, the translational energy plays a classical role. The complication there arises from the fact that r of Eqs. 17-9 and 18-11 is small enough that explicit effects of Fermi-Dirac or Bose-Einstein statistics are of dominating importance. As the temperature is raised, the effects of statistics become less and less, and finally Boltzmann statistics is applicable. Also, the rotational energy thaws out, usually at temperatures a little above the transition to Boltzmann statistics. Rotation gives its classical contribution at temperatures of from a few hundredths to a few tens of degrees Kelvin. Then comes the vibrational energy, which becomes appreciable only at temperatures from a few hundred to a few thousand degrees. Finally, electronic energy levels can be excited at high enough temperatures and can contribute in complicated ways to the specific heat.

Thus, molar heat capacity for an ideal gas is very low at low temperatures, perhaps just $3R/2$. This is because most of the energy modes are frozen; that is, the interval between the energy levels is large with respect to kT. As first the rotational energy thaws out, C_V rises to $5R/2$ for linear molecules or $6R/2$ for non-linear ones. Then as the vibrational levels thaw out, C_V rises until it reaches $(6n - 5)R/2$ for non-linear molecules or $(6n - 6)R/2$ for linear ones.

PROBLEMS

19-1. What are the degeneracies of the following rotational energy levels: (a) 0, (b) $\hbar^2/I$, (c) $6\hbar^2/I$, (d) $20k\Theta_{rot}$?

19-2. Prove the following:

$$\overline{C_V} = \frac{N}{kT^2} [\overline{\epsilon^2} - (\epsilon)^2].$$

19-3. What fraction of diatomic molecules have rotational energy greater than kT?

19-4. What is the ratio of populations of N_2 molecules vibrationally unexcited to those in the first excited vibrational state at 25°C?

19-5. What is the ratio of populations of N_2 molecules rotationally unexcited to those with energy equal to that of the first excited rotational level at 25°C?

19-6. Verify Eq. 19-6 with help of the references given.

19-7. Verify Eq. 19-17 with help of the references given.

19-8. Verify that the high temperature limit of $\bar{\epsilon}_{vib}$ is indeed kT, and not $kT + k\Theta_{vib}/2$.

20 SUMMARY OF IDEAL BOLTZMANN GAS

At this point it is convenient to summarize the results for the statistical thermodynamics of ideal gases. As shown in Sec. 17, when Boltzmann statistics are applicable, the partition function is given very accurately by

$$Q = \frac{1}{N!} q^N. \tag{20-1}$$

The logarithm of Q, from which the thermodynamic variables are obtained, may be written using Eq. 19-4:

$$\ln Q = \ln\left(\frac{1}{N!} q_{trans}^N q_{rot}^N q_{vib}^N q_{elect}^N\right). \tag{20-2}$$

For large N, **Stirling's approximation** is shown by most calculus books to be an excellent representation of $\ln N!$:

$$\ln N! \approx N \ln N - N = N \ln \frac{N}{e}.$$ (20-3)

Therefore, $\ln Q$ becomes simply

$$\ln Q = N \ln\left(\frac{e}{N} q_{\text{trans}} q_{\text{rot}} q_{\text{vib}} q_{\text{elect}}\right),$$ (20-4)

$$\ln Q = N \ln \frac{e}{N} q_{\text{trans}} + N \ln q_{\text{rot}}$$

$$+ N \ln q_{\text{vib}} + N \ln q_{\text{elect}}.$$ (20-5)

The first term in Eq. 20-5 contains both the effects of translation of the molecule as a whole and the effects of particle indistinguishability. This latter is the e/N, coming from the $1/N!$ of Eq. 17-8. The first term was shown by Eq. 18-17 to be

$$\frac{e}{N} q_{\text{trans}} = \frac{eV}{N}\left(\frac{mkT}{2\pi\hbar^2}\right)^{3/2}.$$ (20-6)

This gives, as expected, each *particle's* contribution to the extensive thermodynamic variables as a function of only the average particle density N/V, rather than of either N or V separately.

The second term of Eq. 20-5 gives the rotational contribution to $\ln Q$. It is zero for monatomic gases, is the form of Eq. 19-16 for non-linear polyatomic gases, and is given by Eq. 19-13 for linear polyatomic gases:

$$q_{\text{rot, linear}} = \frac{T}{\sigma\Theta_{\text{rot}}} = \frac{2IkT}{\sigma\hbar^2}.$$ (20-7)

The third term of Eq. 20-5 gives the vibrational contribution to $\ln Q$. It is zero for monatomic gases. For polyatomic gases, there is one contribution of the form of Eq. 19-22 for each normal mode of vibration:

$$q_{\text{vib}} = \frac{e^{-\Theta_{\text{vib}}/2T}}{1 - e^{-\Theta_{\text{vib}}/T}}.$$ (20-8)

The last term of Eq. 20-5 gives the electronic contribution to $\ln Q$. All electronic states whose energies are not much more than kT above the lowest contribute to the sum over states. If there are no such states, only the states of zero energy contribute, and the result is Eq. 19-27:

$$q_{\text{elect}} = g_0.$$

(20-9)

A change in the zero of energy is often incorporated in $\ln Q$, which would make a fifth term in Eq. 20-5. One often chooses the vibrational energy zero, as discussed in connection with Eq. 19-24. A change in energy zero may be accomplished by adding

$$N \ln q_{\text{zero}}$$

(20-10)

to Eq. 20-5, where

$$q_{\text{zero}} = e^{\mathscr{E}/kT},$$

(20-11)

and $\mathscr{E}$ is the new zero of energy relative to the old. In the particular case discussed with Eq. 19-24, the energy of infinite separation is

$$\mathscr{E} = D_0 + \frac{k\Theta_{\text{vib}}}{2}$$

(20-12)

above the bottom of the vibrational potential well, so each vibrational contribution to $\ln Q$ would be corrected by a term

$$q_{\text{zero}} = e^{D_0/kT + \Theta_{\text{vib}}/2T}.$$

(20-13)

This section is concluded by Table 20-1, which summarizes the statistical thermodynamics of an ideal gas of diatomic molecules. Added terms for larger polyatomic molecules are obvious. Contributions to each variable are noted for translation-indistinguishability, rotation, vibration, electronic, and energy zero. This last contribution depends on choice of the zero of energy and is therefore optional. Translation and rotation appear in the classical limit, vibration in the harmonic oscillator approximation. The electronic contributions are calculated simply from Eq. 20-9.

Because of its frequent occurrence in the literature, we note that the expression for $S_{\text{trans-indis}}$ given in the first column of Table 20-1 is often called the *Sackur-Tetrode equation* after the two scientists who formulated it independently.*

It is interesting that the entropy of a monatomic gas may be found by calorimetry, which essentially integrates

$$dS = \frac{\delta q_{\text{rev}}}{T}$$

from almost absolute zero to room temperature. Also, however, S is a

---

* O. Sackur, *Ann. Physik*, **36**, 958 (1911); **40**, 67 (1913). H. Tetrode, *Ann. Physik*, **38**, 434 (1912).

Table 20-I. Contributions to Thermodynamic Variables in a Diatomic Ideal Gas

	trans-indis	rot	vib	elect	zero (of energy)
$\bar{E}$	$\frac{3}{2}NkT$	NkT	$\frac{1}{2}Nk\Theta_{vib} + \dfrac{Nk\Theta_{vib}}{e^{\Theta_{vib}/T}-1}$	0	$-ND_0 - \frac{1}{2}Nk\Theta_{vib}$
$\bar{A}$	$-NkT\ln\left[\dfrac{eV}{N}\left(\dfrac{mkT}{2\pi\hbar^2}\right)^{3/2}\right]$	$-NkT\ln\left(\dfrac{T}{\sigma\Theta_{rot}}\right)$	$\frac{1}{2}Nk\Theta_{vib} + NkT\ln(1 - e^{-\Theta_{vib}/T})$	$-NkT\ln g_0$	$-ND_0 - \frac{1}{2}Nk\Theta_{vib}$
$\bar{\mu}_i$	$-kT\ln\left[\dfrac{V}{N}\left(\dfrac{mkT}{2\pi\hbar^2}\right)^{3/2}\right]$	$-kT\ln\left(\dfrac{T}{\sigma\Theta_{rot}}\right)$	$\frac{1}{2}k\Theta_{vib} + kT\ln(1 - e^{-\Theta_{vib}/T})$	$-kT\ln g_0$	$-D_0 - \frac{1}{2}k\Theta_{vib}$
$\bar{S}$	$Nk\ln\left[\dfrac{e^{5/2}V}{N}\left(\dfrac{mkT}{2\pi\hbar^2}\right)^{3/2}\right]$	$Nk\ln\left(\dfrac{eT}{\sigma\Theta_{rot}}\right)$	$-Nk\ln(1 - e^{-\Theta_{vib}/T}) + \dfrac{Nk\Theta_{vib}}{T(e^{\Theta_{vib}/T} - 1)}$	$Nk\ln g_0$	0
$\overline{C_V}$	$\frac{3}{2}Nk$	Nk	$\dfrac{Nk\Theta_{vib}^2 e^{\Theta_{vib}/T}}{T^2(e^{\Theta_{vib}/T} - 1)^2}$	0	0
$\bar{P}$	$\dfrac{NkT}{V}$	0	0	0	0

$\bar{H} = \bar{E} + \bar{P}V = \bar{E} + NkT; \qquad \bar{G} = \bar{A} + \bar{P}V = \bar{A} + NkT = \sum_i N_i\bar{\mu}_i; \qquad \overline{C_P} = \overline{C_V} + Nk; \qquad \Theta_{rot} = \hbar^2/2Ik; \qquad \Theta_{vib} = \hbar\omega/k.$

state function and may be obtained from statistical mechanics simply by knowing the state; that is, the atomic weight, the total mass, the volume, and the temperature. Historically, this gave a means of fixing the value of Planck's constant from purely macroscopic measurements.

PROBLEMS

20-1. Consider a system that has only two accessible states, a ground state of energy zero and an excited state of energy ϵ. If this system were in equilibrium with a heat bath of temperature T, calculate $\bar{A}$, $\bar{E}$, $\bar{S}$, and $\overline{C_V}$. Sketch a plot of $\overline{C_V}$ versus T.

20-2. Prove that the choice of the zero of energy does not affect $\bar{P}, \overline{C_V}, \overline{C_P}$, or $\bar{S}$.

20-3. What is the molar entropy of helium gas at 298.16°K and one atmosphere pressure?

20-4. Discuss and compare the results you would expect for the thermodynamic functions $\bar{E}$, $\bar{H}$, $\bar{A}$, $\bar{G}$, $\bar{\mu}$, $\bar{S}$, $\overline{C_V}$, and $\overline{C_P}$ for a mole of the following ideal gases: (*a*) Ne at 400°K, (*b*) Ne at 4000°K, (*c*) HBr at 400°K, (*d*) HBr at 4000°K. The degeneracy of the ground state is unity. Utilize Table 19-1. Do not calculate these quantities in detail. What approximation might break down?

20-5. An ideal gas mixture in a volume V is composed of N_a molecules of type a and N_b molecules of type b. Formulate the partition function.

20-6. Find ΔS for the process of combining N_a molecules of type a in a volume V_a with N_b molecules of type b in a volume V_b to form a final mixture of volume $V_a + V_b$. Do the same in the case in which the molecules of type a and type b are actually identical.

20-7. Consider N molecules adsorbed on a surface of area $\mathscr{A}$. They may move freely in the x and y directions, but have no freedom in the z direction. Calculate the translational partition function for the system. The system must perform work to increase the surface area by $d\mathscr{A}$. The part of this work due to the adsorbed molecules is $-\mathscr{P} \, d\mathscr{A}$. Find the equation of state, which relates $\mathscr{P}$, $\mathscr{A}$, and T for non-interacting molecules.

20-8. We claim that q_{elect} at low temperatures is g_0, but is it? Consider as simple a case as a gas of hydrogen atoms. The electronic states of a free hydrogen atom are known, their energies being given by

$$\epsilon_n = -\frac{a}{n^2}.$$

The quantum number n may have the values $1, 2, 3, \ldots$. If there are two possible spin alignments, then g_0 for this atom is 2. What is the value of q_{elect} at any temperature using these energy levels? Discuss the meaning of this. Since the probability that the atom will be in a given state is $e^{-\beta \epsilon(\text{state})}/q_{\text{elect}}$, with this value of q_{elect}, what does this do to the probabilities? Even of the ground state? What has gone wrong?

20-9. Does the degeneracy of the ground electronic state contribute to $\overline{C_V}$ at low temperatures? When might it contribute to $\overline{C_V}$? Explain.

20-10. Prove that the so-called Sackur-Tetrode equation as given by the translation-indistinguishability contribution to $\bar{S}$ is indeed correct, based on the value of Q for an ideal gas.

21 | IDEAL GAS IN A GRAVITATIONAL FIELD

It is easy to extend the treatment of the ideal gas to include the effects of an external gravitational field. For many purposes this field may be neglected, but there are a number of phenomena in which the effects of gravity are by no means negligible.

We first consider a new reduced distribution function, the **one-particle density** $n_1(\mathbf{r})$, defined by

$$n_1(\mathbf{r}) = \int d\mathbf{p}\, f_1(\mathbf{r}, \mathbf{p}). \tag{21-1}$$

The meaning of $n_1(\mathbf{r})$ is the following: The probability that a given particle lies within $d\mathbf{r}$ at $\mathbf{r}$ is expressed by $n_1(\mathbf{r})\, d\mathbf{r}$. The one-particle density is related to the familiar particle density ρ by

$$\rho(\mathbf{r}) = N n_1(\mathbf{r}), \tag{21-2}$$

because of the fact that $\rho(\mathbf{r})$ is defined by the following: The probable number of particles that lie within $d\mathbf{r}$ at $\mathbf{r}$ is given by $\rho(\mathbf{r})\, d\mathbf{r}$.

The only contribution to the energy of a particle which depends on the position is the gravitational potential $\mathscr{V}(\mathbf{r})$. Therefore, $n_1(\mathbf{r})$ and $\rho(\mathbf{r})$ are simply

$$n_1(\mathbf{r}) = a e^{-\mathscr{V}(\mathbf{r})/kT}; \quad \rho(\mathbf{r}) = A e^{-\mathscr{V}(\mathbf{r})/kT}. \tag{21-3}$$

One can often avoid finding the normalization constants by comparing the values of the densities at two different positions as a ratio:

$$\frac{n_1(\mathbf{r}_2)}{n_1(\mathbf{r}_1)} = \frac{\rho(\mathbf{r}_2)}{\rho(\mathbf{r}_1)} = e^{-[\mathscr{V}(\mathbf{r}_2) - \mathscr{V}(\mathbf{r}_1)]/kT}. \tag{21-4}$$

In studying gases, one is often more interested in pressures than in densities. They are easily related to each other through a modification of the ideal gas law,

$$\bar{P} = \frac{N}{V} kT, \tag{21-5}$$

which was derived in Eq. 13-21 for a field-free system. If there is a varying gravitational field, the derivation of Eq. 13-21 must be modified slightly. The tiny region of Fig. 13-3 must be truly infinitesimal. Then, over so small a region, the change in gravitational potential may be neglected. This changes the derivation between Eqs. 13-19 and 13-21 only in replacing $1/V$, the spatial part of f_1, by $n_1(\mathbf{r})$:

$$f_1(\mathbf{r}, \mathbf{p}) = n_1(\mathbf{r})\left(\frac{\beta}{2\pi m}\right)^{3/2} e^{-\beta p^2/2m}. \tag{21-6}$$

This replaces the equation of state, Eq. 13-21, by the more general expression,

$$\bar{P} = Nn_1(\mathbf{r})kT = \rho(\mathbf{r})kT. \tag{21-7}$$

If the gravitational potential arises only from the earth, then $\mathscr{V}(\mathbf{r})$ at a height h is

$$\mathscr{V}(\mathbf{r}) = mgh. \tag{21-8}$$

The acceleration of gravity g has the value 980 cm/sec² at sea level. Use of this with Eqs. 21-4 and 21-7 yields

$$\frac{P(h_2)}{P(h_1)} = \frac{\rho(h_2)}{\rho(h_1)} = e^{-mg(h_2-h_1)/kT}$$

$$= e^{-Mg(h_2-h_1)/RT}. \tag{21-9}$$

Equation 21-9 gives the ratio of the pressures or densities at two different heights in the earth's gravitational field for an ideal gas of molecular weight M, each molecule of which weighs m. The system must be at equilibrium; therefore the temperature must be the same at both heights. Also, the acceleration of gravity g must vary negligibly between the two heights. The density or pressure becomes smaller the higher one goes. For gases with greater molecular weights, the drop-off is more abrupt than for lighter gases. Various forms of Eq. 21-9 are often called the **barometric equation.** The equation may be derived from purely thermodynamic arguments, which ignore the particle nature of the gas completely.

The theory of ideal gases has been applied, interestingly enough, to dilute suspensions of colloidal particles in liquids. Colloidal particles are huge by ordinary molecular standards, from about 10 Å to 10,000 Å. If they are suspended in a liquid, the constant bombardment by molecules of the liquid prevents their settling out under the influence of gravity. In dilute concentration, the colloidal particles may be treated as comprising a gas. The liquid is treated as a continuous medium and is neglected, except for its buoyancy effect on the mass of the colloidal particles.

Of course, real colloidal particles interact with each other; thus the gas is not ideal. It is observed, however, that as any particular property of a colloidal suspension is plotted against concentration, the extrapolated value of this property at zero concentration takes the value it would have if the gas were ideal.

For densities of colloidal particles, Eq. 21-9 is useful in the low density limit,

$$\rho(h_2) = \rho(h_1)e^{-m^*g(h_2-h_1)/kT},\qquad(21\text{-}10)$$

where m^* is the particle weight corrected for buoyancy, that is, the mass of the particle minus the weight of the displaced liquid medium. Many studies of colloidal suspensions have been made using Eq. 21-10, but a major drawback is the relative smallness of the earth's gravitational field.

During the period 1923 to 1925, in order to increase the gravitational field to as much as several hundred thousand g, T. Svedberg developed the ultracentrifuge.† As is known from elementary physics, if a particle of mass m^* is spun ω revolutions per second at a distance x from the axis of revolution, the centrifugal energy is

$$\mathscr{V}_{\text{cent}} = -\tfrac{1}{2}m^*\omega^2x^2.\qquad(21\text{-}11)$$

This may be quickly verified by noting that it yields a centrifugal force

$$F_{\text{cent}} = -\frac{\partial\mathscr{V}_{\text{cent}}}{\partial x} = m^*\omega^2x,\qquad(21\text{-}12)$$

which is probably more familiar to the reader. In this case, instead of Eq. 21-10, one has

$$\rho(x_2) = \rho(x_1)e^{-m^*\omega^2(x_1{}^2-x_2{}^2)/2kT},\qquad(21\text{-}13)$$

or

$$\ln\rho(x_2) = -\frac{m^*\omega^2(x_1{}^2 - x_2{}^2)}{2kT} + \ln\rho(x_1).\qquad(21\text{-}14)$$

One may thus find m^* from the slope of the curve made by plotting $\ln\rho(x)$ against x^2. The ultracentrifuge permits fairly accurate determination of the molecular weight of reasonably small molecules, using Eq. 21-14.

PROBLEMS

21-1. Suppose you are going up in an elevator and your ears pop at the thirtieth floor, about 100 meters above the ground. What pressure change caused your ears to pop? *Note:* For small x, $e^{-x} \approx 1 - x$. The average molecular weight of air is about 29. The temperature could be $300°K$.

† This remarkable instrument and its application to a variety of problems are discussed by T. Svedberg and K. O. Pedersen, *The Ultracentrifuge*, Oxford University Press, London, 1940.

21-2. Consider that at the earth's surface, air is composed mostly of oxygen and nitrogen with average molecular weight of 29. About one part in a thousand, however, is hydrogen with molecular weight of 2. If the air is at about $-10°C$ to all heights, at what height does the concentration of hydrogen equal the concentration of oxygen and nitrogen put together? At 800 km, what is the ratio of the concentration of hydrogen to that of the other species? Assume that Eq. 21-14 is still valid.

21-3. Below what height will be found just half the gas molecules in the earth's gravitational field? Let $\mathscr{V} = mgh$ and let T be constant at $0°C$. The average molecular weight of air is 29.

21-4. Find the density of an ideal gas at some arbitrary point in a cylinder of radius R and length l. The cylinder contains N molecules, each weighing m grams, and rotates about its axis with angular velocity ω. Neglect the external gravitational field.

21-5. Experiments with colloids based on equations as simple as Eq. 21-9 provided some of the first *direct* evidence for the existence of molecules, one of the earliest tests of the statistical mechanics of macroscopic substances, and an accurate determination of Avogadro's number. J. Perrin and coworkers [*Ann. chim. phys.*, **18**, 5 (1909); *Compt. rend.*, **152**, 1380 (1911)] and others determined N_0 from Eq. 21-9. Boltzmann's constant was replaced by R/N_0. The gas constant R was known from work with gases. Their experiments are described by Glasstone [S. Glasstone, *Textbook of Physical Chemistry* (Macmillan and Co., London, 2d ed., 1953), p. 257]. They suspended granules of gamboge, a bright yellow gum resin, of density 1.194 in water at 25°C. Their granules had average radii of 0.368×10^{-4} cm. They found $\rho(h_2)/\rho(h_1) = 10^{0.481}$ for $h_2 - h_1$ of only 0.01 mm. What value of Avogadro's number did they determine?

22   OCCUPATION NUMBERS—
EFFECT OF STATISTICS

In this section the discussion returns to the subject of the first part of Sec. 17. It was stated there that an N-particle quantum state for an ideal gas is determined if the number of particles in each available particle state is given. For fermions, at most only one particle can be in a state; for bosons, any number can be in the same state. In this section the ensemble averages $\overline{N_i}$ of the number of particles in particle state i are found for both fermions and bosons. These are really the *ensemble averages* of the occupation numbers, but most authors call them simply the **occupation numbers** of the particle states. They correspond to what one would *predict* for the number of particles in state i in a system composed of fermions or bosons.

For systems in which the ratio r of Eq. 17-9 is decreased toward unity from something very large, the properties change in important ways due to the fact that the particles are either fermions or bosons. The second and fourth conditions given in Sec. 8 for the validity of the Boltzmann distribution are not fulfilled. The gas is still ideal by the definition of Sec. 12, but $\overline{N}_i$ is no longer simply proportional to $e^{-\beta\epsilon_i}$. Consequently, the ideal gas law no longer is the equation of state for the gas. The occupation numbers found for fermions and bosons must become proportional to $e^{-\beta\epsilon_i}$ only when the ratio r becomes much greater than unity.

A system in equilibrium with a heat bath is represented by an ensemble defining the probability of the jth N-particle quantum state:

$$P_N(j) = \frac{e^{-\beta E_j}}{Q_N}. \tag{22-1}$$

This equation is well defined only when knowledge of what N-particle states are allowed is incorporated in the partition function:

$$Q_N = \sum_{\substack{N\text{-particle} \\ \text{states}}} e^{-\beta E(\text{state})}. \tag{22-2}$$

FERMI-DIRAC STATISTICS

For an ideal gas of fermions, each allowed particle state will have either zero or one particle in it; N different states will always be occupied. The occupation number for fermions is the same as the probability that particle state i be occupied. This probability and the occupation number are found by counting the members of the ensemble with a particle in state i and dividing by the total number of members. The occupation number for fermions, $\overline{N}_{i,FD}$, is therefore

$$\overline{N}_{i,FD} = \sum P_N(\text{state}) = \sum \frac{e^{-\beta E_N(\text{state})}}{Q_N}, \tag{22-3}$$

the sum being over all N-particle quantum states which have particle state i occupied. If the notation $Q_N{}'$ and $Q_N{}^0$ be used for *the sums over all N-particle states having particle state i occupied or unoccupied respectively,* then Eq. 22-3 becomes

$$\overline{N}_{i,FD} = \frac{Q_N'}{Q_N} = \frac{Q_N'}{Q_N{}^0 + Q_N'} \tag{22-4}$$

$$= \frac{1}{(Q_N{}^0/Q_N') + 1}, \tag{22-5}$$

$$\overline{N}_{i,FD} = \frac{1}{(Q_N{}^0/Q_{N-1}^0)e^{\beta\epsilon_i} + 1}. \tag{22-6}$$

Equation 22-4 takes advantage of the fact that the set of *all* N-particle states may be viewed as the sum of those with particle state i *occupied* plus those with it *unoccupied*. In Eq. 22-5, the numerator and denominator are divided by Q_N'. In Eq. 22-6, the fact that Q_N' has particle state i occupied is recognized by factoring $e^{-\beta\epsilon_j}$ out of Q_N', since it occurs in every term. The remainder is equivalent to the sum over all $(N-1)$-particle states having particle state i unoccupied, so it is given the symbol Q_{N-1}^0.

The ratio in the denominator of Eq. 22-6 depends on choice of particle state i only through the requirement that none of the N or $N-1$ particles be in that state. The value of this ratio will not change noticeably for different choices of i if the temperature is high enough that the N lowest lying particle states are not solidly filled. This is true even for small N, but if N is enormous, the ratio is essentially independent of i even at absolute zero. Therefore, the ratio may be taken as independent of choice of particle state i:

$$F = \frac{Q_{N-1}^0}{Q_N{}^0} \approx \frac{Q_{N-1}}{Q_N}, \tag{22-7}$$

and Eq. 22-6 becomes simply

$$\boxed{\overline{N}_{i,FD} = \frac{1}{F^{-1}e^{\epsilon_i/kT} + 1} = \frac{Fe^{-\epsilon_i/kT}}{1 + Fe^{-\epsilon_i/kT}}.} \tag{22-8}$$

The value of the ratio F may be obtained by normalization:

$$\sum_i \overline{N}_{i,FD} = N = \sum_i \frac{1}{F^{-1}e^{\epsilon_i/kT} + 1}, \tag{22-9}$$

although evaluation of such a summation is rarely easy.

BOSE-EINSTEIN STATISTICS

For an ideal gas of bosons, every possible number of particles in state i will be represented by some N-particle quantum states. The occupation number for state i is the ensemble average of the number of particles in state i:

$$\overline{N}_{i,BE} = 1 \cdot \sum_{\substack{N\text{-particle states} \\ (1\,\text{particle in } i)}} P_N(\text{state}) + 2 \cdot \sum_{\substack{N\text{-particle states} \\ (2\,\text{particles in } i)}} P_N(\text{state})$$

$$+ 3 \cdot \sum_{\substack{N\text{-particle states} \\ (3\,\text{particles in } i)}} P_N(\text{state}) + \cdots \tag{22-10}$$

$$= 1 \cdot \frac{Q_N{}'}{Q_N} + 2 \cdot \frac{Q_N{}''}{Q_N} + 3 \cdot \frac{Q_N{}'''}{Q_N} + \cdots. \tag{22-11}$$

The primed notation is an obvious extension, the number of primes being the number of particles in state i. This expression may be put into more convenient form by recognizing the fact that the set of *all* N-particle states may be viewed as the sum of those with one particle in i, those with two particles in i, those with three, etc:

$$\overline{N}_{i,BE} = \frac{Q_N{}' + 2Q_N{}'' + 3Q_N{}''' + \cdots}{Q_N{}^0 + Q_N{}' + Q_N{}'' + \cdots}. \tag{22-12}$$

In almost any conceivable situation, the terms in the series in numerator and denominator of Eq. 22-12 get smaller as the series progress. This is because, as more particles are fixed in state i, there are fewer others which may be in the other states. Thus there are fewer N-particle states over which to sum.

The reader may verify that Eq. 22-12 is identical to

$$\overline{N}_{i,BE} = \frac{Q_N{}'\left(1 + 2\dfrac{Q_N{}''}{Q_N{}'} + 3\dfrac{Q_N{}'''}{Q_N{}'} + \cdots\right)}{Q_N{}^0\left(1 + 2\dfrac{Q_N{}'}{Q_N{}^0} + 3\dfrac{Q_N{}''}{Q_N{}^0} + \cdots\right) - Q_N{}'\left(1 + 2\dfrac{Q_N{}''}{Q_N{}'} + 3\dfrac{Q_N{}'''}{Q_N{}'} + \cdots\right)} \tag{22-13}$$

simply by multiplying Eq. 22-13 out. In the numerator and the second series of the denominator, $e^{-\beta\epsilon_i}$ may be canceled in each term:

$$\overline{N}_{i,BE}$$

$$= \frac{Q_N{}'\left(1 + 2\dfrac{Q'_{N-1}}{Q^0_{N-1}} + 3\dfrac{Q''_{N-1}}{Q^0_{N-1}} + \cdots\right)}{Q_N{}^0\left(1 + 2\dfrac{Q_N{}'}{Q_N{}^0} + 3\dfrac{Q_N{}''}{Q_N{}^0} + \cdots\right) - Q_N{}'\left(1 + 2\dfrac{Q'_{N-1}}{Q^0_{N-1}} + 3\dfrac{Q''_{N-1}}{Q^0_{N-1}} + \cdots\right)}. \tag{22-14}$$

Except for the difference between Q_N and Q_{N-1}, the series in the parentheses are identical and may be canceled. This difference might be noticeable in some of the last terms, but when N is large the effect on the sums is negligible:

$$\overline{N}_{i,BE} = \frac{Q_N{}'}{Q_N{}^0 - Q_N{}'},$$ (22-15)

$$\overline{N}_{i,BE} = \frac{1}{(Q_N{}^0/Q_{N-1}^0)e^{\beta\epsilon_i} - 1}.$$ (22-16)

This resembles Eq. 22-6. An argument similar to what led to Eq. 22-7 can be made here. Only when the temperature is so low that all the particles are crowded into a handful of lowest energy levels could the ratio in the denominator depend on choice of state i. Thus, the ratio may be written

$$B = \frac{Q_{N-1}^0}{Q_N{}^0} \approx \frac{Q_{N-1}}{Q_N}$$ (22-17)

and Eq. 22-16 is

$$\boxed{\overline{N}_{i,BE} = \frac{1}{B^{-1}e^{\epsilon_i/kT} - 1} = \frac{Be^{-\epsilon_i/kT}}{1 - Be^{-\epsilon_i/kT}}.}$$ (22-18)

Just as with F in Eq. 22-9, the value of B is fixed by normalization:

$$\sum_i \overline{N}_{i,BE} = N = \sum_i \frac{1}{B^{-1}e^{\epsilon_i/kT} - 1}.$$ (22-19)

BOLTZMANN STATISTICS

The last case of interest is that in which the occupation numbers are all very small, much less than unity. This means there are a great many more states available to each particle than there are particles. This is clearly the case, discussed in Sec. 17, in which Boltzmann statistics are applicable. It is clear from Eqs. 22-8 and 22-18 that in this case, if $\overline{N}_i$ is small, then F or B times the exponential must be small. Therefore, this term may be neglected in the denominators where it is added to or subtracted from unity. Thus, $\overline{N}_i$ for fermions becomes identical to $\overline{N}_i$ for bosons, and they take the simple exponential form

$$\boxed{\overline{N}_{i,B} = Ae^{-\epsilon_i/kT}.}$$ (22-20)

The value of A is fixed by normalization:

$$\sum_i \overline{N}_{i,B} = N = A \sum_i e^{-\epsilon_i/kT}.$$ (22-21)

23   FERMI-DIRAC AND BOSE-EINSTEIN GASES

In this section, the statistical mechanical expressions for the various thermodynamic properties of ideal fermion or boson gases are found by a method analogous to that of Sec. 9. The statistical thermodynamics is here based on occupation numbers, in contrast to the use of the partition function in Secs. 17 to 20 for the Boltzmann gas. The Boltzmann limit of these results is of course identical to the results of Secs. 17 to 20. The partition function approach has the advantage of being valid in all cases, in particular, for systems other than ideal gases. However, within the partition function framework it is hard to incorporate the definition of a quantum state for fermions or bosons. On the other hand, the occupation number approach directly incorporates the correct definition of a quantum state, but it is limited to ideal gases. One must choose the approach best suited to the problem at hand.

Occupation numbers for both fermions and bosons may be considered together by writing Eqs. 22-8 and 22-18 thus:

$$\overline{N_i} = \frac{De^{-\beta\epsilon_i}}{1 \pm De^{-\beta\epsilon_i}}. \tag{23-1}$$

We have chosen D as compromise notation for the parameters F and B. The value of D will of course be different in the two cases, except in the Boltzmann limit. The upper sign applies for fermions, the lower sign for bosons.

This joint notation may be used to express the normalization condition, Eqs. 22-9 and 22-19, and also the ensemble average of the energy of the system:

$$N = \sum_i \overline{N_i} = \sum_i \frac{De^{-\beta\epsilon_i}}{1 \pm De^{-\beta\epsilon_i}} \; ; \tag{23-2}$$

$$\bar{E} = \sum_i \epsilon_i \overline{N_i} = \sum_i \frac{D\epsilon_i e^{-\beta\epsilon_i}}{1 \pm De^{-\beta\epsilon_i}}. \tag{23-3}$$

Since either one or the other of Eqs. 23-2 and 23-3 is sufficient to fix D, the two equations together should permit an interpretation of D in terms of thermodynamic quantities.

Relating D to the thermodynamic variables of the system is accomplished for fermions and bosons by a method similar to that used in Sec. 9. In this case, the place of the logarithm of the partition function is taken by the function Ψ, defined thus:

$$\Psi \equiv \pm\sum_i \ln(1 \pm De^{-\beta\epsilon_i}). \tag{28-4}$$

That this is the obvious replacement for $\ln Q$ will be shown later. In Sec. 9, $\ln Q$ is a function of temperature, the constraints on the system, and the number of particles, that is, of β, V, and N. In the procedure of Sec. 9, when a reversible change was made in $\ln Q$, N was kept fixed. Had N also been allowed to vary in Eq. 9-6, then the equivalent of Eq. 11-14 for $\bar{\mu}$ would have been found directly, as the reader may quickly verify. The function Ψ also depends on β and V and has N-dependence in the parameter D.

In place of Eq. 9-6 for $d\ln Q$, the value of Ψ is altered by explicit changes in β, V (or the ϵ's), and D (or N and the ϵ's):

$$d\Psi = \frac{\partial\Psi}{\partial\beta}\,d\beta + \sum_i \frac{\partial\Psi}{\partial\epsilon_i}\,d\epsilon_i + \frac{\partial\Psi}{\partial D}\,dD \tag{23-5}$$

$$= \pm\sum_i \frac{\mp D\epsilon_i e^{-\beta\epsilon_i}}{1 \pm De^{-\beta\epsilon_i}}\,d\beta \pm \sum_i \frac{\mp D\beta e^{-\beta\epsilon_i}}{1 \pm De^{-\beta\epsilon_i}}\,d\epsilon_i$$

$$\pm \sum_i \frac{\pm e^{-\beta\epsilon_i}}{1 \pm De^{-\beta\epsilon_i}}\,dD, \tag{23-6}$$

$$d\Psi = -\bar{E}\,d\beta - \beta\,\overline{dE} \pm \frac{N}{D}\,dD. \tag{23-7}$$

The identifications in passing from Eq. 23-6 to 23-7 were based on Eqs. 23-2 and 23-3. Two identities are employed here, instead of just Eq. 9-8:

$$d(\bar{E}\beta) = \bar{E}\,d\beta + \beta\,d\bar{E}, \tag{23-8}$$

$$d(N\ln D) = \frac{N}{D}\,dD + \ln D\,dN. \tag{23-9}$$

The quantity $\overline{dE}$ in Eq. 23-7 is the negative of the reversible work, $-\overline{\delta w}$, as is discussed following Eq. 9-7. Employing Eqs. 23-8 and 23-9 permits turning Eq. 23-7 into the desired form:

$$d\Psi = \beta\,d\bar{E} - d(\bar{E}\beta) + \beta\,\overline{\delta w} + d(N\ln D) - \ln D\,dN,$$

$$d\bar{E} = kT\,d(\Psi + \bar{E}\beta - N\ln D) - \overline{\delta w} + kT\ln D\,dN. \tag{23-10}$$

This is compared with the general *thermodynamic* equation for dE in a reversible change, including a change in number of particles:

$$dE = T \, dS - \delta w + \mu \, dN, \tag{23-11}$$

where μ is the chemical potential. Comparison of Eqs. 23-10 and 23-11 permits writing a statistical mechanical expression for both the chemical potential and the entropy:

$$\bar{\mu} = kT \ln D = -kT \ln \frac{Q_N}{Q_{N-1}}. \tag{23-12}$$

The chemical potential thus appears to be a rather peculiar average which expresses the effect of adding one more particle to the ideal gas. The energy scale for $\bar{\mu}$ is the same as that for the energy of a particle; in particular, these scales have the same zero. If Eq. 23-12 is solved for D,

$$D = e^{\bar{\mu}/kT}. \tag{23-13}$$

The entropy is obtained in a similar way:

$$d\bar{S} = k \, d(\Psi + \bar{E}\beta - N \ln D). \tag{23-14}$$

The same argument as was used in going from Eq. 9-13 to 9-15 gives

$$\bar{S} = k\Psi + \frac{\bar{E}}{T} - Nk \ln D. \tag{23-15}$$

By using Eq. 23-13, Eq. 23-4 for Ψ may be rewritten:

$$\boxed{\Psi = \pm \sum_i \ln \left(1 \pm e^{(\bar{\mu} - \epsilon_i)/kT} \right).} \tag{23-16}$$

Similarly, the two equivalent ways of rewriting the occupation numbers, Eq. 23-1, are

$$\boxed{\overline{N_i} = \frac{1}{e^{(\epsilon_i - \bar{\mu})/kT} \pm 1} = \frac{e^{(\bar{\mu} - \epsilon_i)/kT}}{1 \pm e^{(\bar{\mu} - \epsilon_i)/kT}}.} \tag{23-17}$$

Before concluding this section, it is worth noting a few thermodynamic results obtainable in general from Ψ. Passing from Eq. 23-5 to 23-7 proved that

$$\boxed{\bar{E} = -\left(\frac{\partial \Psi}{\partial \beta} \right)_{V, D}.} \tag{23-18}$$

It also established that

$$\beta \, \overline{\delta w} = \beta \bar{P} \, dV = \sum_i \frac{\partial \Psi}{\partial \epsilon_i} \, d\epsilon_i = \frac{\partial \Psi}{\partial V} \, dV. \tag{23-19}$$

Comparing the second and fourth terms of Eq. 23-20 shows

$$\beta \bar{P} = \left(\frac{\partial \Psi'}{\partial V}\right)_{D,\beta}; \tag{23-20}$$

$$\boxed{\bar{P} = kT\left(\frac{\partial \Psi'}{\partial V}\right)_{D,T}.} \tag{23-21}$$

It is an easy matter for the reader to establish that

$$\frac{\bar{E}}{\bar{P}} = -\beta \frac{\partial \Psi'/\partial \beta}{\partial \Psi'/\partial V} = \tfrac{3}{2} V \tag{23-22}$$

in the case that ϵ_i is proportional to $V^{-\frac{2}{3}}$. This is indeed the volume dependence of ϵ_i for the translational energy of free particles in a cubical box, as shown by Eq. 18-6. Therefore, for an ideal monatomic gas,

$$\bar{P}V = \tfrac{2}{3}\bar{E} \tag{23-23}$$

for both fermions and bosons, as well as in the Boltzmann limit.

It is interesting to note the difference in $\bar{E}$ (or pressure, since they are proportional) caused by the explicit effect of Fermi-Dirac or Bose-Einstein statistics at low temperatures. Consider first the normalization condition

$$\sum_i \bar{N}_i = N = \sum_i \frac{1}{e^{(\epsilon_i - \bar{\mu})/kT} \pm 1}. \tag{23-24}$$

For fermions, each term in the summation has a larger denominator than it does for bosons. Therefore, in order to offset this effect, $\bar{\mu}$ must be larger for fermions than for bosons. However, examination of Eq. 23-17 shows that $\bar{N}_i$ becomes damped only for particle energies larger than $\bar{\mu}$. This occurs at higher energies for fermions than for bosons; therefore the ensemble average of the system energy,

$$\bar{E} = \sum_i \epsilon_i \bar{N}_i = \sum_i \frac{\epsilon_i e^{(\bar{\mu}-\epsilon_i)/kT}}{1 \pm e^{(\bar{\mu}-\epsilon_i)/kT}}, \tag{23-25}$$

is greater for fermions than for bosons.

This is not surprising. Considering Table 17-1, we may think of kT as a measure of the upper bound, below which the energies of the occupied states must lie. As the temperature is lowered, the particles are squeezed into the fewer and fewer states with energy below kT. Fermions are restricted to only one particle per quantum state, while any number of bosons may be in the same state. Thus, in order to accommodate all the particles, fermions must go into higher energy levels than bosons; since all bosons may, if they wish, go into a single quantum state. In the extreme case of $T = 0°K$, the N fermions occupy the N states of lowest energy while all N bosons are in the single state of lowest energy. The energy (thus, the pressure) of a fermion gas is consequently higher than it would be if the particles were bosons. These results are often said to reflect a "repulsion of the fermions due to quantum mechanical *exchange forces*" or an "attraction of the bosons leading to a quantum mechanical *condensation*." This terminology is unfortunate because of the connotations these phrases have for most people.

The only reason it is harder to treat fermions or bosons correctly than to use Boltzmann statistics is that the summation of Eq. 23-16 to find Ψ is so much more difficult to perform than the summation of the simple exponential in Boltzmann statistics. However, in the next two sections, special cases of particular interest are briefly treated.

PROBLEMS

23-1. Prove Eq. 23-23.
23-2. Consideration of the form of Eq. 23-17 is sufficient to prove what requirement on the sign of $\bar{\mu}$ for bosons?

24   METALS—THE ELECTRON GAS

One may use the statistical mechanics of the ideal Fermi-Dirac gas to gain considerable insight into the properties of metals. This is done by introducing a greatly oversimplified model of the metallic structure. The metal is treated as if it were composed of the outer valence electrons of its atoms and of the resulting positive ions. The positive ions form a lattice through which the electrons are completely free to move. The plus and minus charges of the ions and electrons are assumed to neutralize each other with only negligible forces resulting on the electrons. Such a model is certainly crude, but as a first approximation to the mechanical structure of metals, its simplicity and predictive successes make it well worth studying.

As mentioned in Sec. 17, electrons are fermions. Whether or not the electron gas may be described by Boltzmann statistics depends on the ratio r of Eq. 17-9. This ratio is calculated in Sec. 18 for structureless particles in a box. The conclusion, Eq. 18-10, would be correct for electrons except for the fact that each one may be in one of two states simply by virtue of its spin.* For electrons, therefore, r is simply twice the value given by Eq. 18-10.

The temperature Θ at which r equals unity is called the **characteristic temperature of degeneration** and is interesting to calculate for an electron gas:

$$r = 1, \tag{24-1}$$

$$\frac{2\pi}{6N}\left(\frac{2Mk\Theta}{N_0}\right)^{3/2}\frac{V}{\pi^3 h^3} = 1, \tag{24-2}$$

$$\Theta = \frac{3^{2/3}\pi^{4/3}h^2 N_0\rho^{2/3}}{2Mk}. \tag{24-3}$$

For metals, a reasonable estimate of ρ is obtained by assuming that each metal atom furnishes one valence electron and that a molar volume is perhaps 6 cm^3. There would then be about 10^{23} valence electrons per cubic centimeter of the metal. The molecular weight of an electron is only about 1/1840; therefore,

$$\Theta = \frac{3^{2/3}\pi^{4/3}(1.054 \times 10^{-27}\,\text{erg-sec})^2(6.02 \times 10^{23}\,\text{mole}^{-1})(10^{23}\,\text{cm}^{-3})^{2/3}}{2(1840)^{-1}\,\text{g-mole}^{-1}(1.38 \times 10^{-16}\,\text{erg-deg}^{-1})},$$

$$\Theta = 29{,}700\,\text{deg} \quad \text{or} \quad \text{about } 3 \times 10^4\,\text{deg}. \tag{24-4}$$

Thus, a metal would have to be heated to almost a million degrees before Boltzmann statistics would yield a good approximation to the partition function of the electron gas.

Room temperatures T are so much less than Θ that they may be treated as minor perturbations from absolute zero. At absolute zero, the occupation number for fermions,

$$\overline{N_i} = \frac{1}{e^{(\epsilon_i - \bar{\mu})/kT} + 1}, \tag{24-5}$$

will be zero if ϵ_i exceeds the chemical potential at absolute zero, $\bar{\mu}_0$. This is because the exponential in the denominator of Eq. 24-5 is infinitely large. On the other hand, if ϵ_i is less than $\bar{\mu}_0$, the exponential vanishes

---

* The spin quantum number is either $+\frac{1}{2}$ or $-\frac{1}{2}$; see any of the quantum mechanics references.

and $\overline{N_i}$ is unity. Therefore, at absolute zero,

$$\overline{N_i} = 1, \quad \epsilon_i < \bar{\mu}_0;$$
$$\overline{N_i} = 0, \quad \epsilon_i > \bar{\mu}_0.$$

(24-6)

This case is called **complete degeneration** of the electron gas. The electrons completely fill the lowest lying set of energy levels available to them, which are all those below $\bar{\mu}_0$. It has become common to call $\bar{\mu}_0$ the **Fermi limiting energy**, or the **Fermi level**. Electrons with energy $\bar{\mu}_0$ are said to lie on the surface of the **Fermi sea**. Electrons with energy

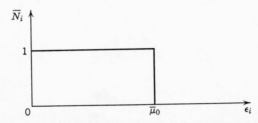

Fig. 24-1. Plot of occupation number against energy of the states ϵ_i for an electron gas at absolute zero.

less than $\bar{\mu}_0$ are in the Fermi sea, below the surface by a depth $\bar{\mu}_0 - \epsilon_i$. In Fig. 24-1, the occupation number is plotted against the energy of the states ϵ_i for an electron gas at absolute zero.

The chemical potential at absolute zero, $\bar{\mu}_0$, is easily found from the energy of the particle state that lies Nth from the lowest. Consider the quantum number space, discussed in conjunction with Fig. 18-1. The number of states represented by an eighth of a sphere in this space is twice the volume of the eighth of the sphere. The factor 2 comes from the two possible spins. This number of states must equal N:

$$2 \cdot \tfrac{1}{8} \cdot \tfrac{4}{3}\pi n_{max}^3 = N,$$

(24-7)

$$n_{max} = \left(\frac{3N}{\pi}\right)^{1/3}.$$

(24-8)

Therefore, using Eq. 18-6,

$$\bar{\mu}_0 = \epsilon_{max} = \frac{\pi^2 \hbar^2}{2ma^2} n_{max}^2 = \frac{\pi^2 \hbar^2}{2mV^{2/3}} n_{max}^2,$$

$$\bar{\mu}_0 = \frac{\pi^2 \hbar^2}{2m}\left(\frac{3N}{\pi V}\right)^{2/3}.$$

(24-9)

At absolute zero, the average energy of an electron will be less than $\bar{\mu}_0$, because most electrons lie below the surface of the Fermi sea. It is easy to determine that in fact $\bar{\epsilon}$ is $3\bar{\mu}_0/5$. The proof starts from the first part of Eq. 23-3:

$$\bar{E} = \sum_i \epsilon_i \overline{N_i}. \tag{24-10}$$

The occupation numbers at absolute zero are given by Eq. 24-6, so the summation in Eq. 24-10 is simply the sum of ϵ_i over the N lowest lying particle states. Again we are interested in the eighth of a sphere of radius n_{max} in quantum number space. However, this time each unit of volume contributes not unity, but its appropriate energy,

$$\epsilon(n) = \frac{\pi^2 \hbar^2}{2ma^2} n^2, \tag{24-11}$$

times 2, because of the two allowed spins:

$$\bar{E} = 2 \int d\mathbf{n} \, \frac{\pi^2 \hbar^2}{2ma^2} n^2, \tag{24-12}$$

$$= \frac{\pi^2 \hbar^2}{ma^2} \int_0^{n_{max}} n^4 \, dn \int_0^{\pi/2} \sin\theta \, d\theta \int_0^{\pi/2} d\chi \tag{24-13}$$

$$= \frac{\pi^2 \hbar^2}{ma^2} \left(\frac{n_{max}^5}{5}\right)(1)\left(\frac{\pi}{2}\right) \tag{24-14}$$

$$= \frac{\pi^3 \hbar^2}{10ma^2} \left(\frac{3N}{\pi}\right)^{5/3} = \frac{3N\pi^2 \hbar^2}{10m} \left(\frac{3N}{\pi V}\right)^{2/3}, \tag{24-15}$$

$$\bar{E} = \tfrac{3}{5}N\bar{\mu}_0. \tag{24-16}$$

This leads to an enormous value of the pressure, as calculated from Eq. 23-24:

$$\bar{P} = \frac{2\bar{E}}{3V} = \tfrac{2}{5}\rho\bar{\mu}_0. \tag{24-17}$$

By comparison of Eq. 24-9 with Eq. 24-3,

$$\bar{\mu}_0 = k\Theta. \tag{24-18}$$

Thus, the pressure may be estimated in the same way Eq. 24-4 was obtained:

$$\bar{P} = \tfrac{2}{5}\rho k\Theta \tag{24-19}$$

$$= \tfrac{2}{5}(10^{23} \text{ cm}^{-3})(1.38 \times 10^{-16} \text{ erg-deg}^{-1})$$

$$\times (3 \times 10^4 \text{ deg})(10^{-6} \text{ atm/dyne-cm}^{-2}),$$

$$\bar{P} \approx 3 \times 10^5 \text{ atm.} \tag{24-20}$$

This huge pressure is balanced by the attraction between the electrons and the positive ions of the lattice. It is this balance which holds the metal together.

The above calculations have been made considering the temperature to be zero. Because the ratio T/Θ is so very small, this is an excellent approximation. In particular, the energy $\bar{E}$ is almost independent of temperature for small T/Θ, and consequently the specific heat of the electrons is negligible. This is because as the temperature is slightly

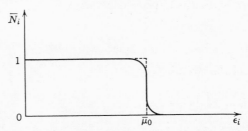

Fig. 24-2. Plot of occupation number against energy of the states ϵ_i for an electron gas at finite temperature $T \ll \Theta$.

increased, only a relatively few more particle states are made available to electrons. Only a few electrons quite near the surface of the Fermi sea can move up into excited states. The bulk of the electrons remain below $\bar{\mu}_0$ even for temperatures large compared to 300°K but small compared to Θ. Before the advent of quantum mechanics, it was one of the riddles of statistical mechanics why the electron gas did not contribute to the heat capacity of metals.*

It is true that at finite temperatures, T/Θ is not truly zero, and the diagram of Fig. 24-1 should look more like that of Fig. 24-2. The width of the range of deviation of the two diagrams is of order kT. Thus, there is actually a very small contribution to $\overline{C_V}$ by the electrons, since some few of them do find enough energy to go into levels above the surface of the Fermi sea.†

PROBLEMS

24-1. Using Eq. 23-15, find $\bar{S}$ for an electron gas at absolute zero. Is the result surprising?

24-2. Based on the value found for F in Eq. 22-7, prove that at absolute zero F is indeed $e^{\beta \epsilon_{max}}$, as used above. If F of Sec. 22 is equated to $e^{\beta \bar{\mu}}$, discuss what this implies about the meaning of $\bar{\mu}$.

* For example, see J. H. Jeans, *The Dynamical Theory of Gases*, 4th ed., 1925, reprinted by Dover Publications, Inc., 1954, Sec. 524.

† This problem is treated in detail by Mayer and Mayer, Chap. 16.

25   RADIATION—THE PHOTON GAS

If any substance is "in equilibrium at a given temperature," then within it, in equilibrium with its matter, is certain electromagnetic radiation. This radiation may be thought of as a gas of non-interacting photons. When viewed as a particle, the photon of radiation is a boson of zero rest mass. In this section some of the properties of such equilibrium radiation will be studied by applying statistical mechanics to the photon gas.

It is convenient to define as the *system* an evacuated cavity or hole inside the piece of matter. The only content of the system is the equilibrium radiation characteristic of the matter at the walls. In this way, the radiation alone may be studied with minimum complications.

Unlike a gas of material particles, photons may be either created or absorbed by the matter with which they interact. *Any* number of photons *might* be in the system at a given time. When one sums over all N-particle states to obtain the partition function for the photon gas, one must include terms representing every possible value of N—0, 1, 2, . . . — essentially an infinite number. Only then will the partition function be a sum over *all possible quantum states*. This inclusion of terms for all possible values of N has one immediate consequence; *there is no longer any dependence in Q on the number of photons N. All* possible numbers are contained in Q. Therefore, the chemical potential of a photon gas at equilibrium, as given by Eq. 11-17, must be zero:

$$\bar{\mu} = -kT\left(\frac{\partial \ln Q}{\partial N}\right)_{T,V} = 0. \qquad (25\text{-}1)$$

In summary: The fact that the chemical potential of a photon gas is zero at equilibrium is a direct consequence of the fact that photons may be created or destroyed at the walls of the system. An analogous situation will be seen in the discussion of chemical equilibrium, Sec. 30.

A photon is characterized by its energy,

$$\epsilon_i = \hbar\omega_i, \tag{25-2}$$

where ω_i is the angular velocity (sometimes called *frequency*) in radians per second. The population of photons of a given frequency is found from Eq. 23-17 to be simply

$$\overline{N}_i = \frac{1}{e^{\hbar\omega_i/kT} - 1}, \tag{25-3}$$

since $\bar{\mu}$ is zero.

There is an extraordinarily large number of allowed frequencies; their density is so great that summing over the allowed frequencies is always performed by integration. For example, the ensemble average of the number of photons present in the system, $\overline{N}$, is found by multiplying Eq. 25-3 by the number of quantum states with frequency between ω and $\omega + d\omega$ and integrating over frequency. It is therefore necessary to determine the number of quantum states with frequency between ω and $\omega + d\omega$ for photons in a box of volume V.

The logical approach to this problem might seem to lie in solving Schrödinger's equation, 18-5, for a photon in a box, getting the mass from Einstein's equation, $\epsilon = \hbar\omega = mc^2$. Unfortunately, the problem is not that simple, since Eq. 18-5 is valid only at non-relativistic speeds where m is the rest mass of the particle. Schrödinger did propose the correct relativistic counterpart to Eq. 18-5,* which we shall obtain in a completely different, but more intuitive, way.

WAVE EQUATION FOR PHOTONS

Let us define a **wave** as *any* function of position which retains its shape, but moves at a constant velocity. At time zero, this function is $\Phi_0(x)$, where for simplicity we consider only one dimension. Let this disturbance be moving at velocity v in the plus x direction. An observer watching at x will see the disturbance moving from left to right. At time t, what he sees is what was located a distance vt to his left at time zero. Therefore, the time dependence of the disturbance at a point x is given simply by the equation

$$\Phi(x, t) = \Phi_0(x - vt). \tag{25-4}$$

---

* The simple ideas of relativity are given by Eisberg, Chap. 1. The relativistic Schrödinger equation is treated by Schiff, Sec. 42.

Now, if one demands that the form of the wave, $\Phi_0(x)$, be a sine or cosine with wave length λ,

$$\Phi_0(x) = A \sin\left[a + \frac{2\pi x}{\lambda}\right],$$

$$\Phi(x, t) = A \sin\left[a + \frac{2\pi(x - vt)}{\lambda}\right]. \tag{25-5}$$

The time independent differential equation satisfied by such a wave may be found by differentiating Eq. 25-5 twice with respect to x:

$$\frac{\partial^2\Phi}{\partial x^2} = -\left(\frac{2\pi}{\lambda}\right)^2 A \sin\left[a + \frac{2\pi(x - vt)}{\lambda}\right],$$

$$\frac{\partial^2\Phi}{\partial x^2} = -\left(\frac{2\pi}{\lambda}\right)^2 \Phi. \tag{25-6}$$

Since v/λ is the number of complete cycles per second, $2\pi v/\lambda$ is the angular velocity ω in radians per second (sometimes called *frequency*):

$$\frac{\partial^2\Phi}{\partial x^2} = -\frac{\omega^2}{v^2}\Phi. \tag{25-7}$$

Solution of Eq. 25-7 gives the spatial part of the wave function.

In electromagnetic theory, photons are viewed as wave disturbances propagating at a velocity c. The three-dimensional counterpart to Eq. 25-7 for photons is

$$\nabla^2\varphi = -\frac{\omega^2}{c^2}\varphi. \tag{25-8}$$

Equation 25-6 is often called the **Helmholtz equation** and is the *counterpart for photons to the time independent Schrödinger equation* for a material particle in a box, Eq. 18-5:

$$\nabla^2\psi = -\frac{2m\epsilon}{\hbar^2}\psi. \tag{25-9}$$

The analogy between Eqs. 25-8 and 25-9 also extends to their boundary conditions—both φ and ψ must be zero at the walls of the box. The mathematical problem posed by Eq. 25-8 is identical to that posed by Eq. 25-9. Therefore, the solution of Eq. 25-9 given by Eq. 18-6 may be appropriated directly, simply by replacing the $2m\epsilon/\hbar^2$ of the Schrödinger equation with the ω^2/c^2 of the Helmholtz equation:

$$\epsilon(n_x, n_y, n_z) = \frac{\pi^2\hbar^2}{2ma^2}(n_x^2 + n_y^2 + n_z^2), \tag{25-10}$$

$$\frac{2m\epsilon}{\hbar^2} = \frac{\pi^2}{a^2}(n_x^2 + n_y^2 + n_z^2), \tag{25-11}$$

$$\frac{\omega^2}{c^2} = \frac{\pi^2}{a^2}(n_x^2 + n_y^2 + n_z^2).$$

The result is simpler in the quantum number space of Fig. 18-1:

$$\frac{\omega^2}{c^2} = \frac{\pi^2}{a^2}n^2, \qquad \frac{\omega}{c} = \frac{\pi}{a}n, \tag{25-12}$$

$$\frac{d\omega}{c} = \frac{\pi}{a}dn. \tag{25-13}$$

The volume in quantum number space between n and $n + dn$ is that of one-eighth of the spherical shell at n of thickness dn:

$$\tfrac{1}{8} \cdot 4\pi n^2 \, dn. \tag{25-14}$$

If one quantum state is associated with each unit of volume in quantum number space, then the number of quantum states for photons in a box of volume V with frequency between ω and $\omega + d\omega$ is obtained from Eq. 25-14 using Eqs. 25-12 and 25-13:

$$\tfrac{1}{8} \cdot 4\pi \left(\frac{a^2\omega^2}{\pi^2c^2}\right)\left(\frac{a \, d\omega}{\pi c}\right) = \frac{V\omega^2 \, d\omega}{2\pi^2c^3} \tag{25-15}$$

This result is valid not only for electromagnetic waves, but also for others such as sound waves in crystals. This is discussed in Sec. 29.

In the case of photons, there are twice as many states as shown by Eq. 25-15 because of the two possible polarizations for photons which would otherwise be in the same state. Since each state has a population given by Eq. 25-3, the number of photons, $d\overline{N}_\omega$, within the frequency range ω to $\omega + d\omega$ is the product of Eq. 25-3 and twice Eq. 25-15:

$$d\overline{N}_\omega = \frac{V\omega^2 \, d\omega}{\pi^2c^3(e^{\hbar\omega/kT} - 1)}. \tag{25-16}$$

RADIANT ENERGY AND PRESSURE

The energy $d\overline{E}_\omega$ of the radiation in the frequency range ω to $\omega + d\omega$ is simply the number of photons in that range, $d\overline{N}_\omega$, times the energy of each, $\hbar\omega$:

$$d\overline{E}_\omega = \frac{V\hbar\omega^3\,d\omega}{\pi^2 c^3 (e^{\hbar\omega/kT} - 1)}\,.$$ (25-17)

This equation is correct for radiation in equilibrium with matter. It is called **Planck's radiation law** and was very important historically. It was first presented in 1900 as "an interpolation formula which resulted

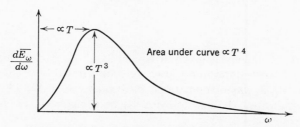

Fig. 25-1. Plot of spectral density against frequency.

from a lucky guess,"* joining the two limits which were well known at that time: $\hbar\omega \gg kT$ (Wien's empirical law) and $\hbar\omega \ll kT$ (the Rayleigh-Jeans law). Its subsequent interpretation as implying *quantized* energies of a field of oscillators was the first introduction of quantum effects into physics. This opened the door to the rapid development of quantum mechanics and all of modern physics in the twentieth century.

In Fig. 25-1, the change in energy with frequency, $d\overline{E}_\omega/d\omega$, sometimes called the **spectral density**, is plotted as a function of ω. The area under this curve between two values of ω gives the energy of the radiation in the frequency range bounded by the ω's. In Probs. 25-1 and 25-2 it is shown that the frequency of maximum spectral density, ω_{max}, and the spectral density at that frequency are given by

$$\omega_{max} = 2.822\,\frac{kT}{\hbar}\,;$$ (25-18)

$$\left(\frac{\partial\overline{E}_\omega}{\partial\omega}\right)_{max} = \frac{1.42 V k^3 T^3}{\pi^2 c^3 \hbar^2}\,.$$ (25-19)

* Planck's Nobel Prize inaugural address, quoted by Sommerfeld, p. 148.

Equation 25-18 is often called **Wien's displacement law**. The range of frequencies in which the most energy is contained becomes higher as the temperature increases. The total radiation energy contained in V, $\bar{E}_{\text{total}}$, increases very rapidly with increasing temperature, as is found by integrating Eq. 25-17 over all frequencies:

$$\bar{E}_{\text{total}} = \int_0^\infty \frac{Vh\omega^3 \, d\omega}{\pi^2 c^3 (e^{\hbar\omega/kT} - 1)} \tag{25-20}$$

$$= \frac{Vh}{\pi^2 c^3} \int_0^\infty \left(\frac{\hbar\omega}{kT}\right)^3 \left(\frac{kT}{\hbar}\right)^3 d\left(\frac{\hbar\omega}{kT}\right) \left(\frac{kT}{\hbar}\right) \frac{1}{e^{\hbar\omega/kT} - 1}$$

$$= \frac{Vk^4 T^4}{\pi^2 c^3 \hbar^3} \int_0^\infty \frac{x^3 \, dx}{e^x - 1},$$

$$\bar{E}_{\text{total}} = \frac{V\pi^2 k^4 T^4}{15 c^3 \hbar^3}. \tag{25-21}$$

The value of the integral is given in Appendix C, Eq. C-9. This result is the so-called **Stefan-Boltzmann law**. A proportionality of E_{total} to the fourth power of T was demonstrated by Boltzmann in 1884 by thermodynamic arguments. It had previously been deduced by Stefan on empirical grounds.

The radiation exerts a pressure on the walls of its enclosure, which may be determined by the method of Prob. 23-1, once the volume dependence of ϵ is known. This is obtained directly from Eq. 25-12:

$$\epsilon = \hbar\omega = \frac{\pi c \hbar}{a} n; \tag{25-22}$$

$$\epsilon \propto V^{-\frac{1}{3}}. \tag{25-23}$$

The method of Prob. 23-1 then shows

$$\bar{P}V = \tfrac{1}{3}\bar{E}, \tag{25-24}$$

$$\bar{P} = \frac{\bar{E}}{3V} = \frac{\pi^2 k^4 T^4}{45 c^3 \hbar^3} = 2.4 \times 10^{-21} T^4 \text{ atm.} \tag{25-25}$$

BLACK BODY RADIATION

If one had a volume filled with radiation at temperature T, the contents could be studied by making a small hole in the body and observing the radiation emitted. If the hole is small enough, the photon leakage does not appreciably disturb the equilibrium distribution within the volume.

This is another example of *effusion*, this time of photons. Any radiation striking the hole from outside will pass in and be absorbed by the walls without readmission. Since absorbing surfaces usually are called *black*, the radiation effusing out of the hole is called **black body radiation**.

The effusion process for photons is illustrated by Fig. 25-2, which resembles Fig. 13-3. The radiation within the volume is completely isotropic; that is, photons are equally likely to be going in any direction.

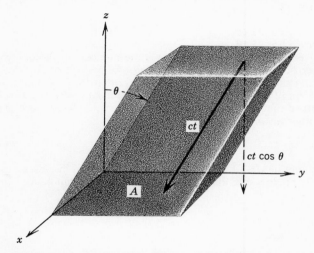

Fig. 25-2. Parallelepiped of impact for photons with a hole of area A.

The *spectral density per unit volume per unit solid angle* $e_0(\omega)$ is simply $d\overline{E_\omega}/d\omega$ divided by $4\pi V$ (4π being the total number of steradians):

$$e_0(\omega) = \frac{1}{4\pi V} \frac{d\overline{E_\omega}}{d\omega} = \frac{\hbar \omega^3}{4\pi^3 c^3 (e^{\hbar\omega/kT} - 1)}. \qquad (25\text{-}26)$$

The $e_0(\omega)$ may be multiplied by the volume per second, $Ac \cos\theta$, of the parallelepiped containing radiation which passes through the hole. If it is then integrated over the solid angle of a hemisphere, the result is the *spectral density of the total radiation emitted per second, $J(\omega)$*:

$$J(\omega) = \frac{\hbar A \omega^3}{4\pi^3 c^2 (e^{\hbar\omega/kT} - 1)} \int_0^{\pi/2} \sin\theta \cos\theta \, d\theta \int_0^{2\pi} d\chi \qquad (25\text{-}27)$$

$$= \frac{\hbar A \omega^3}{4\pi^3 c^2 (e^{\hbar\omega/kT} - 1)} \int_0^1 x \, dx \cdot 2\pi$$

$$= \frac{\hbar A \omega^3}{4\pi^2 c^2 (e^{\hbar\omega/kT} - 1)}. \qquad (25\text{-}28)$$

The *total black body radiation emitted per unit area per second*, J, is merely $1/A$ times the integral of this over all frequencies. By analogy with the proof of Eq. 25-21, this is simply

$$J = \frac{c\bar{E}}{4V} = \frac{\pi^2 k^4 T^4}{60 c^2 \hbar^3}.$$ (25-29)

PROBLEMS

25-1. Prove Eq. 25-18.

25-2. Prove Eq. 25-19.

25-3. Over which frequency interval is the number of photons greater than the number of states available, so there must be multiple occupancy of states? Over which states is the converse true? Prove that for these latter frequencies, the equivalent of Eq. 25-17 using Boltzamnn statistics would be correct.

25-4. Prove that *any* wave, Eq. 25-4, has its time dependence given by the so-called *wave equation:*

$$\frac{\partial^2 \Phi}{\partial x^2} = \frac{1}{v^2} \frac{\partial^2 \Phi}{\partial t^2}.$$

What assumption about the *time* dependence of Φ is necessary to leave the spatial part of Φ a solution of the one-dimensional Helmholtz equation, Eq. 25-7?

PART III

SPECIAL TOPICS

26   DENSE FLUIDS—SEMI-CLASSICAL PARTITION FUNCTION

Many real gases approach ideality closely enough that their thermodynamic properties may be found from the ideal gas partition function. As the density of a gas is increased and the average intermolecular distance becomes smaller, however, more particles come within each other's fields of force. For ideal gases the intermolecular potential energy (Fig. 12-1) is zero. Its proper treatment is needed for real gases and for liquids, because it is the intermolecular potentials that give these substances their interesting properties. In this section the partition function including intermolecular potentials is discussed formally. In Secs. 27 and 28 this partition function is applied to dense gases.

Intermolecular potential energies are most easily expressed as functions of the relative positions of the particles involved. Thus for dense fluids it is convenient to use a phase space involving the classical coordinates and momenta of the molecules, instead of simply their translational quantum numbers. This procedure is discussed under the title *semi-classical mechanics* in Sec. 5. Classical positions and momenta may be introduced in two ways. The one-particle reduced distribution function of Eq. 13-1 may be replaced by the appropriate two-particle function, giving probabilities of simultaneous positions and momenta of two particles. This is the approach taken in non-equilibrium statistical mechanics where the partition function is useless.

Equilibrium, however, is often best approached through the semi-classical partition function. As mentioned in Sec. 5, probabilities in a semi-classical ensemble relate to continuous $\mathbf{r}$'s and $\mathbf{p}$'s and to discrete internal quantum states for the N molecules. Instead of using the N-particle probability P_N, one uses the N-particle distribution function f_N, defined thus: The probability that one particle be located within $d\mathbf{r}_1$ at $\mathbf{r}_1$ and have its momentum lie within $d\mathbf{p}_1$ at $\mathbf{p}_1$ and have internal quantum state characterized by n_1, *and* that a second particle be located within $d\mathbf{r}_2$ at $\mathbf{r}_2$ and have its momentum . . . , for all N particles simultaneously is

$$f_N(\mathbf{r}_1, \mathbf{r}_2, \ldots, \mathbf{r}_N, \mathbf{p}_1, \mathbf{p}_2, \ldots, \mathbf{p}_N, n_1, n_2, \ldots, n_N) \, d\mathbf{r}_1 \, d\mathbf{r}_2 \cdots d\mathbf{p}_1 \cdots d\mathbf{p}_N.$$

$$(26\text{-}1)$$

Several shorthand conventions for writing this are in common use. The set of N position vectors is written as $\mathbf{r}^N$; the set of N momentum vectors as $\mathbf{p}^N$, the set of N internal quantum states as n^N, and the product of volume elements as $d\mathbf{r}^N\,d\mathbf{p}^N$. Then, Eq. 26-1 is identical to

$$f_N(\mathbf{r}^N, \mathbf{p}^N, n^N)\, d\mathbf{r}^N d\mathbf{p}^N. \tag{26-2}$$

For a system in equilibrium with a heat bath, the exponential distribution function,

$$f_N(\mathbf{r}^N, \mathbf{p}^N, n^N) = a e^{-\beta E(\mathbf{r}^N, \mathbf{p}^N, n^N)}, \tag{26-3}$$

arises for the same reasons P_N was shown to be exponential in Sec. 7. Furthermore, proofs identical to those of Secs. 9 to 11 relate the ensemble averages of the thermodynamic variables to the partition function Q, the only difference being that the sum over states must be an integral of f_N over $d\mathbf{r}^N$ and $d\mathbf{p}^N$ and a sum over the various internal states n^N. This is often called a semi-classical **phase integral**, instead of a partition function.

However, it is not so simple as just writing down this sum over n^N and integrating over $d\mathbf{r}^N$ and $d\mathbf{p}^N$ and calling the result Q. It may be convenient to use classical mechanics to describe certain features of the ensemble, but it is still quantum mechanics that determines what a state of the system is! The phase integral we wish to use must be modified so that it actually gives the same result as would be found by summing over the set of N-particle quantum states.

In Sec. 18 it was found that Q factored into one part representing the centers of mass of the molecules, $Q_{\text{c.m.}}$, and one part representing their internal energies, Q_{int}:*

$$Q = Q_{\text{c.m.}} \cdot Q_{\text{int}}. \tag{26-4}$$

No change is made in Q_{int} on changing to a semi-classical ensemble, so we shall just consider $Q_{\text{c.m.}}$. For an ideal gas, Eqs. 18-4 and 18-17 showed this to be

$$Q_{\text{c.m.}} = \frac{1}{N!} q_{\text{trans}}^N = \frac{1}{N!}\left[V\left(\frac{mkT}{2\pi\hbar^2}\right)^{3/2}\right]^N. \tag{26-5}$$

The classical phase integral over $\mathbf{r}$'s and $\mathbf{p}$'s is proportional to

$$\int d\mathbf{r}^N\,d\mathbf{p}^N e^{-\beta E(\mathbf{r}^N, \mathbf{p}^N)} = \int d\mathbf{p}^N \exp\left(-\beta \sum_{i=1}^N p_i^2/2m\right)\int d\mathbf{r}^N e^{-\beta U(\mathbf{r}^N)}, \tag{26-6}$$

where U is the intermolecular potential energy of the configuration of

---

* This factorization is only an approximation for non-ideal gases. The reason is that the intermolecular potential between two particles is a function of the internal states of the particles. The independence between the two, implied by Eq. 26-4, is therefore non-existent.

particles. One takes U to be a function only of the positions of the particles, which is certainly an approximation. Each of the N momentum integrals yields the factor $(2\pi mkT)^{3/2}$, as shown in Prob. 13-1. For an ideal gas, U is zero, and each of the N configuration integrals yields simply the factor V. Thus, for an ideal gas, Eq. 26-6 gives

$$[V(2\pi mkT)^{3/2}]^N, \tag{26-7}$$

which differs from $Q_{c.m.}$, Eq. 26-5, by being $N!\,(2\pi\hbar)^{3N}$ times too large. The classical integral must therefore be divided by this factor to make it correspond with the correct quantum mechanical result:

$$Q_{c.m.} = \frac{1}{N!\,(2\pi\hbar)^{3N}} \int d\mathbf{p}^N \exp\left(-\beta \sum_{i=1}^{N} p_i{}^2/2m\right) \int d\mathbf{r}^N e^{-\beta U(\mathbf{r}^N)}. \tag{26-8}$$

The $N!$ may be viewed as expressing the indistinguishability of the particles, and the $(2\pi\hbar)^{3N}$ the fact that a small volume τ in phase space corresponds to approximately $\tau/(2\pi\hbar)^{3N}$ quantum states. Taken in the other way, the statement that a quantum state is associated with a finite volume, $(2\pi\hbar)^{3N}$, in phase space is one form of the Heisenberg uncertainty principle.*

Clearly, use of Eq. 26-8 is a description of the ensemble in terms of Boltzmann statistics. It is convenient to separate the configuration integral from the rest of the semi-classical partition function, which presents no new problem. The results are summarized below:

$$Q_{\text{semi-cl}} = Q_{c.m.} \cdot Q_{\text{int}}; \tag{26-9}$$

$$Q_{\text{semi-cl}} = Q_{\text{kinetic}} \cdot Q_{\text{config}} \cdot Q_{\text{int}}; \tag{26-10}$$

$$Q_{\text{kinetic}} = \frac{1}{N!}\left(\frac{mkT}{2\pi\hbar^2}\right)^{3N/2}; \tag{26-11}$$

$$Q_{\text{config}} = \int d\mathbf{r}^N e^{-\beta U(\mathbf{r}^N)}; \tag{26-12}$$

$$Q_{\text{int}} = \sum_{n^N} e^{-\beta E_{\text{int}}(n^N)}. \tag{26-13}$$

The total intermolecular energy of a system, U, is often approximated as being the sum of separate contributions from each pair of particles in the system:

$$U = \sum_{i<j=1}^{N} U_{ij}(\mathbf{r}_{ij}). \tag{26-14}$$

---

* See any of the quantum mechanics and most of the statistical mechanics references, especially Eisberg, Chap. 6; d'Abro, pp. 654-666.

The notation on the summation means that both indices run from 1 to N, but that i must always be less than j. This is to avoid counting one contribution twice, that is, as U_{ij} and as U_{ji}.

Use of Eq. 26-14 means that the interaction potential between particles i and j does not change when particle k comes up close to one or both of them, or even when particle k really smacks one of them in a good hard collision. Clearly, particle k's presence would distort the electron clouds of particles i and j and thus change their interaction potential. That is the kind of thing neglected by use of Eq. 26-14. The direct interaction between particle k and the other two is of course still contained in Eq. 26-14 in the terms U_{ik} and U_{jk}. At worst, use of Eq. 26-14 probably just removes the sharp edge of accuracy from theoretical calculations of properties of liquids or quite dense gases. However, even using Eq. 26-14, drastic simplifications are still involved in these calculations, so one need not worry much about Eq. 26-14 when there are so many better things to worry about.

With the approximation of pairwise additive intermolecular potential, the configuration integral is

$$Q_{\text{config}} = \int d\mathbf{r}^N \exp\left[-\beta \sum_{i<j=1}^{N} U_{ij}(\mathbf{r}_{ij}) \right]. \tag{26-15}$$

The problem of approximating the value of Eq. 26-15 for various potentials to find the properties of dense gases and liquids is a current research problem in statistical mechanics.

27   DENSE GASES— VIRIAL EQUATION OF STATE

In this section the equation of state of a dense gas is studied. The expression for the second virial coefficient is obtained in terms of the intermolecular potential energy.

The expected macroscopic pressure in a system is given by Eq. 11-21:

$$\bar{P} = kT\left(\frac{\partial \ln Q}{\partial V}\right)_{T,N}. \tag{27-1}$$

The only term in Q as given by Eq. 26-10 which depends on volume is the configuration integral:

$$\bar{P} = kT\left(\frac{\partial \ln Q_{\text{config}}}{\partial V}\right)_{T,N},$$ (27-2)

$$\bar{P} = kT\left(\frac{\partial}{\partial V}\right)_{T,N} \ln\left\{\int d\mathbf{r}^N \exp\left[-\beta \sum_{i<j=1}^{N} U_{ij}(\mathbf{r}_{ij})\right]\right\}.$$ (27-3)

Equation 27-3 is the equation of state for any fluid, provided only that Boltzmann statistics are applicable and that the assumption of pairwise additive intermolecular potential energy, Eq. 26-14, is reasonable. Much work has gone into evaluating the integrals arising in Eq. 27-3 for various forms of the intermolecular potential, $U_{ij}(\mathbf{r}_{ij})$. In general, the problem is of immense difficulty, which accounts for the fact that a rigorous theory of the liquid state, based on Eq. 27-3, has yet to be developed.

For the problem of dense gases, in which the particle density is in some sense small, progress can be made by expanding Eq. 27-3 in powers of the density. Even this is by no means trivial, and we do it here only to the first correction term beyond the ideal gas law.

The integrand of Eq. 27-3 is the exponential of a sum of $\frac{1}{2}N(N-1)$ terms. Since the exponential of a sum factorizes, this integrand may be written as

$$\exp\left(-\beta \sum_{i<j=1}^{N} U_{ij}\right) = \prod_{i<j=1}^{N} [e^{-\beta U_{ij}}].$$ (27-4)

The notation in Eq. 27-4 is commonly used for a *product* of terms, for example,

$$\prod_{i<j=1}^{4} z_{ij} = z_{12} \cdot z_{13} \cdot z_{14} \cdot z_{23} \cdot z_{24} \cdot z_{34}.$$ (27-5)

Now, since

$$e^z = 1 + \sum_{n=1}^{\infty} \frac{z^n}{n!},$$ (27-6)

Eq. 27-4 may be rewritten

$$\exp\left(-\beta \sum_{i<j=1}^{N} U_{ij}\right) = \prod_{i<j=1}^{N}\left[1 + \sum_{n=1}^{\infty} \frac{(-\beta U_{ij})^n}{n!}\right].$$ (27-7)

We thus end up with the exponential expressed as the product of $\frac{1}{2}N(N-1)$ different infinite series. Needless to say, analysis of Eq. 27-7 is extremely complicated.

The first term in the product, Eq. 27-7, is unity, arising from the unity of every single one of the $\frac{1}{2}N(N-1)$ series. When this is integrated over $d\mathbf{r}^N$, the result is simply V^N.

Next, consider only those terms which involve *just* particles 1 and 2— none other. They arise from the unities of each series except the series for particles 1 and 2, and they are

$$\sum_{n=1}^{\infty} \frac{(-\beta U_{12})^n}{n!} = e^{-\beta U_{12}} - 1. \tag{27-8}$$

When this set of terms, Eq. 27-6, is integrated over $d\mathbf{r}^N$, the result is independent of the fact that it is particles 1 and 2 which were considered. The same result would be found for every other possible combination of two particles. Thus, there are $\frac{1}{2}N(N-1)$ sets of terms present in Eq. 27-7 which involve *just two different particles*, and they give the following contribution to the integral in Eq. 27-3:

$$\frac{1}{2}N(N-1)\int d\mathbf{r}^N [e^{-\beta U_{ij}(\mathbf{r}_{ij})} - 1]$$

$$= \frac{1}{2}N(N-1)V^{(N-2)}\int d\mathbf{r}_i \, d\mathbf{r}_j [e^{-\beta U_{ij}(\mathbf{r}_{ij})} - 1]. \tag{27-9}$$

Since the integrand is a function only of the *relative* coordinate $\mathbf{r}_{ij}$, it is convenient to change variables from $\mathbf{r}_i$ and $\mathbf{r}_j$ to

$$\mathbf{R}_{ij} = \frac{1}{2}(\mathbf{r}_i + \mathbf{r}_j); \quad \mathbf{r}_{ij} = \mathbf{r}_i - \mathbf{r}_j, \tag{27-10}$$

where $\mathbf{R}_{ij}$ is the position of the center of mass of the two particles, and $\mathbf{r}_{ij}$ is the position of particle i as seen from particle j. The identity of volume elements,

$$d\mathbf{r}_i \, d\mathbf{r}_j = d\mathbf{R}_{ij} \, d\mathbf{r}_{ij}, \tag{27-11}$$

was shown in the discussion of Eq. 15-6 for the similar transformation in velocity space. The integral over $d\mathbf{R}_{ij}$ yields another factor V if the volume is much greater than the range of the intermolecular forces. Thus, Eq. 17-9 reduces to

$$\frac{1}{2}N(N-1)V^{(N-1)}\int d\mathbf{r}_{ij}[e^{-\beta U_{ij}(\mathbf{r}_{ij})} - 1] \tag{27-12}$$

$$\equiv -N(N-1)V^{(N-1)}B(T). \tag{27-13}$$

For ease of notation we have defined

$$\boxed{B(T) = -\frac{1}{2}\int d\mathbf{r}_{ij}[e^{-\beta U_{ij}(\mathbf{r}_{ij})} - 1].} \tag{27-14}$$

This quantity is shown below to be the second virial coefficient.

Next consider all those terms in Eq. 27-7 which involve *just* U_{12} and U_{34}. They are

$$\left[\sum_{m=1}^{\infty} \frac{(-\beta U_{12})^m}{m!}\right] \cdot \left[\sum_{n=1}^{\infty} \frac{(-\beta U_{34})^n}{n!}\right] = (e^{-\beta U_{12}} - 1)(e^{-\beta U_{34}} - 1), \tag{27-15}$$

in complete analogy with Eq. 27-8. When this set of terms is integrated over $d\mathbf{r}^N$, the result again is independent of the labels on the particles. There are $N(N-1)(N-2)(N-3)$ or $N!/(N-4)!$ ways of choosing quartets of particles, but the requirement $i < j$ must be considered. Contributions from both U_{12} and U_{21} may not both be counted; similarly with U_{34} and U_{43}. This means $N!/(N-4)!$ must be multiplied by $1/2^2$. Also, simply inverting the order of the two parentheses in Eq. 27-15 does not lead to a new contribution. Accounting for this multiplies $N!/(N-4)$ by $1/2!$. One concludes that the sum of all terms in Eq. 27-7 which involve just two pairs of particles, no particle in more than one pair, gives the following contribution to the integral in Eq. 27-3:

$$\frac{N!}{(N-4)!\,2!\,2^2} \int d\mathbf{r}^N (e^{-\beta U_{ij}} - 1)(e^{-\beta U_{kl}} - 1)$$

$$= \frac{N!\,V^{N-2}}{(N-4)!\,2!\,2^2} \int d\mathbf{r}_{ij}\,d\mathbf{r}_{kl}(e^{-\beta U_{ij}} - 1)(e^{-\beta U_{kl}} - 1)$$

$$= \frac{N!\,V^{N-2}[-2B(T)]^2}{(N-4)!\,2!\,2^2} = \frac{N!\,V^{N-2}[-B(T)]^2}{(N-4)!\,2!}, \qquad (27\text{-}16)$$

in complete analogy with the formulation of Eq. 27-13.

The generalization of the above is immediate: The sum of all terms in Eq. 27-7 which involve zero, one, two, three, ... pairs of particles, no particle in more than one pair, gives the following contribution to the integral in Eq. 27-3:

$$V^N + \sum_{\nu=1}^{\sim N/2} \frac{N!\,V^{N-\nu}[-B(T)]^\nu}{(N-2\nu)!\,(\nu)!}. \qquad (27\text{-}17)$$

For the moment, let us stop the analysis of contributions from Eq. 27-7 with these. The terms being neglected all involve integrals with three or more particles' positions coupled in an integrand. Using this much in Eq. 27-3 yields an approximation $\bar{P}_2$ to the pressure. The derivative of the logarithm is the derivative of Eq. 27-17,

$$NV^{N-1} + \sum_{\nu=1}^{\sim N/2} \frac{N!\,(N-\nu)V^{N-\nu-1}[-B(T)]^\nu}{(N-2\nu)!\,(\nu)!}, \qquad (27\text{-}18)$$

divided by Eq. 27-17.

When Eq. 27-18 is divided by Eq. 27-17, a simplification occurs, as the reader will verify by longhand division in Prob. 27-6. The pressure proves to be

$$\bar{P}_2 = kT\left[\frac{N}{V} + \frac{N(N-1)}{V^2}\,B(T) + \begin{array}{l}\text{terms of higher}\\\text{order in } N/V\end{array}\right]. \qquad (27\text{-}19)$$

Since N/V is assumed small, we shall retain only the first correction term in N/V. The others may be neglected. Furthermore, it is consistent with this approximation to the pressure to neglect all the rest of the terms from Eq. 27-7. For example, for terms in which three particles' positions are coupled, the introduction of the third particle reduces by one the number of factors V resulting from the position integrals. It also introduces another factor of approximately N, the number of ways of picking the additional particle. Thus, terms involving additional particles must be of higher order in N/V. For the same reason, even if explicit three-body effects were included in the intermolecular potential energy, Eq. 26-14, the first such contribution would already be of higher order in N/V.

Since the difference between N and $N - 1$ is negligible, Eq. 27-19 may be rewritten, completely consistent with an expansion of the pressure in powers of N/V, showing the first correction to the ideal gas law:

$$\bar{P}_2 = \frac{NkT}{V}\left[1 + \frac{N}{V} B(T)\right]. \qquad (27\text{-}20)$$

Expansion of the pressure in increasing powers of the density has long been used to interpret experimental data:

$$P = \frac{NkT}{V}\left[1 + \frac{N}{V} B(T) + \frac{N^2}{V^2} C(T) + \frac{N^3}{V^3} D(T) + \cdots\right]. \qquad (27\text{-}21)$$

This equation is called the **virial equation** of state of a gas. The function $B(T)$ is called the **second virial coefficient** and is given in terms of the intermolecular potential by Eq. 27-14. The function $C(T)$ is the third virial coefficient, and so on.

The pressure in a gas will be given by Eq. 27-20 with the second virial coefficient given by Eq. 27-14 whenever Boltzmann statistics are applicable and the particle density is small. This latter requirement is meaningless unless one knows *with respect to what* N/V must be small. In order to determine this, we note that the integrand of Eq. 27-14 is zero where U_{ij} is zero; thus the size of $B(T)$ is of the order of the "volume" of a molecule. Therefore, the correction to ideal gas behavior displayed by Eq. 27-20 is of the order of the ratio of the molecular volume (volume in which the intermolecular potential energy is significant) to the average volume per molecule in the system, V/N. Further terms in the virial expansion would be of higher order in the ratio of the effective volume of a molecule to the average volume, V/N, available to the molecule. It is this ratio which must be small in order for $\bar{P}_2$ to represent $\bar{P}$.

One can continue treating terms in Eq. 27-7 that involve more and more particles in order to find the higher virial coefficients in terms of the intermolecular potentials.* The virial equation is a series of corrections to the *ideal gas* law. For this reason, at *liquid* densities it does not converge, and it becomes enormously complicated.

PROBLEMS

27-1. One analytic form of $U_{ij}(\mathbf{r}_{ij})$ that is often used because of its simplicity is the so-called *square well potential*, defined by

$$U_{ij}(\mathbf{r}_{ij}) = \infty, \quad 0 < r_{ij} < \sigma, \text{ all angles};$$

$$U_{ij}(\mathbf{r}_{ij}) = -\epsilon, \quad \sigma < r_{ij} < R\sigma, \text{ all angles};$$

$$U_{ij}(\mathbf{r}_{ij}) = 0, \quad r_{ij} > R\sigma.$$

Sketch the square well potential and compare with Fig. 12-1. Calculate the second virial coefficient for the square well potential. Discuss the result, noting especially that as ϵ approaches zero, the molecules approach hard rigid spheres.

27-2. Another analytic form of $U_{ij}(\mathbf{r}_{ij})$ is the so-called *Lennard-Jones (6-12) potential*, defined by

$$U_{ij}(\mathbf{r}_{ij}) = 4\epsilon\left[\left(\frac{\sigma}{r}\right)^{12} - \left(\frac{\sigma}{r}\right)^{6}\right].$$

Sketch this potential and compare with Fig. 12-1. It is used because it is a good two-parameter approximation to the actual form of many intermolecular potentials. At what multiple of σ is r large enough that U_{ij} is only $\frac{1}{100}$ as deep as its maximum depth.?

27-3. Instead of using Eq. 27-21, it is sometimes convenient to use another form of the virial expansion,

$$PV = N[kT + B'(T)P + C'(T)P^2 + D'(T)P^3 + \cdots].$$

Calculate $B'(T)$ and $C'(T)$ in terms of the virial coefficients in Eq. 27-21.

27-4. If several species of molecules $i, j, \ldots$ are present in the system, $B_{ij}(T)$ is defined like Eq. 27-14, except i and j may refer to different molecular species. Interpret the equation

$$B(T) = \sum_i \sum_j x_i x_j B_{ij}(T),$$

where x means mole fraction. Why is this equation correct? Why does it include both B_{ij} and B_{ji}? Consider a few simple examples.

27-5. Extend Prob. 20-7 to the first correction for non-ideal behavior.

27-6. Divide longhand the first three terms of Eq. 27-18 by the first three of Eq. 27-17 and verify the result, Eq. 27-19.

---

* The method is described by Mayer and Mayer, Chap. 13, and is reviewed by E. E. Salpeter, *Ann. Phys.* (N.Y.), **5**, 183 (1958).

28

DENSE GASES—
VAN DER WAALS' EQUATION

The familiar van der Waals equation of state,

$$\left(P + \frac{N^2 a}{V^2}\right)(V - Nb) = NkT, \tag{28-1}$$

has proved very useful, with proper choice of the parameters a and b, for correlating the properties of dense gases, even up to the point of condensation. In this section, the conditions under which the van der Waals equation follows from statistical mechanics are investigated.

First, Eq. 28-1 must be multiplied out and put in the form of a virial expansion, Eq. 27-21:

$$PV - PNb + \frac{N^2 a}{V} - \frac{N^3 ab}{V^2} = NkT, \tag{28-2}$$

$$PV\left(1 - \frac{Nb}{V}\right) = NkT - \frac{N^2 a}{V} + \frac{N^3 ab}{V^2}. \tag{28-3}$$

The expansion, Eq. 19-21, may be used for the $1/(1 - Nb/V)$, and all terms of higher order in N/V may be dropped:

$$P = \frac{NkT}{V}\left[1 - \frac{Na}{VkT} + \frac{Nb}{V} + \cdots\right],$$

$$P = \frac{NkT}{V}\left[1 + \frac{N}{V}\left(b - \frac{a}{kT}\right) + \cdots\right]. \tag{28-4}$$

It thus appears, on comparing Eq. 28-4 with 27-20, that whenever $B(T)$ as given by Eq. 27-14 may be approximated by $b - a/kT$, then van der Waals' equation would be expected to give a decent representation of a moderately dense gas. Under what conditions, then, might $B(T)$ be so expressed;

$$\tfrac{1}{2}\int d\mathbf{r}[1 - e^{-\beta U(\mathbf{r})}] \approx b - \frac{a}{kT}? \tag{28-5}$$

For many molecules, the interaction potential $U(\mathbf{r})$ may be treated as spherically symmetric and having the general shape of the curves shown in Fig. 12-1. This is sketched in Fig. 28-1*a*, and the resulting forms of $e^{-\beta U}$ and $1 - e^{-\beta U}$ are shown in Figs. 28-1*b* and 28-1*c*. The temperature chosen in Fig. 28-1 is such that $\epsilon \approx kT/3$. The dotted vertical line furthest

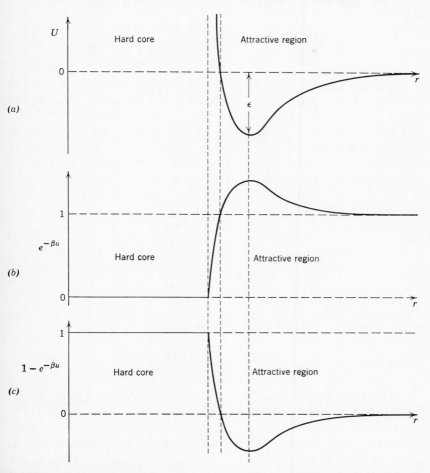

Fig. 28-1. Plots of useful functions of typical intermolecular potential U versus distance of separation r.

to the left is not necessarily the value of r for which U becomes infinite. It is merely the value of r for which U/kT is large enough to make $e^{-U/kT}$ appear as zero on the scale used in Fig. 28-1*b*. The curve of Fig. 28-1*b* does not actually *equal* zero until U is truly infinite, but even for $U = 4kT$, $e^{-\beta U}$ has become $1/e^4$ or 0.018.

As shown by Fig. 28-1c, the integration over r in Eq. 28-5 may be split into two parts. The first is the region in which the integrand is positive. This is the hard core of the molecule and has almost no β-dependence whatever. The integral over this hard core volume yields essentially a constant, b:

$$\tfrac{1}{2}\int_{\substack{\text{hard}\\ \text{core}}} d\mathbf{r}[1 - e^{-\beta U(r)}] \approx \tfrac{1}{2}\int_{\substack{\text{hard}\\ \text{core}}} d\mathbf{r} \approx b. \qquad (28\text{-}6)$$

The second part of the integration volume is the region of attraction of the two particles and gives a negative contribution to the integral. In

Table 28-1. Table of ratios ϵ/k for various gases

Gas	$\epsilon/k(°K)$
Ne	20
A	70
Kr	98
N_2	54
CO_2	119
C_2H_6	244
C_3H_8	347
C_2H_4	222
CH_3Cl	470
NH_3	692
H_2O	1260

ϵ is the estimated depth of the intermolecular potential energy curve. From Hirschfelder, Curtiss, and Bird, p. 160.

order to perform this integration, an approximation must be made. If the equation being derived is valid only for gases at moderate temperature, it is reasonable to suppose that the depth of the potential well ϵ in Fig. 28-1a is less than kT. If it were greater, then many particles on colliding with others would not have enough energy to separate afterward, thus leading to at least partial condensation. A table of estimates of ϵ/k for several substances is given in Table 28-1. For temperatures well above these values, the entire attractive region of the intermolecular potential is characterized by having

$$\beta U(r) \ll 1. \qquad (28\text{-}7)$$

As a result of this, an expansion of the exponential of Eq. 28-5 in the form of Eq. 27-6 may be stopped after the second term:

$$1 - e^{-\beta U(r)} \approx 1 - [1 - \beta U(r)] = \beta U(r). \tag{28-8}$$

The constant β is not involved in the integral over the attractive region, and this integral yields a negative constant, $-a$, times β:

$$\tfrac{1}{2}\int_{\substack{\text{attractive} \\ \text{region}}} d\mathbf{r}\,[1 - e^{-\beta U(r)}] \approx \tfrac{1}{2}\int_{\substack{\text{attractive} \\ \text{region}}} d\mathbf{r}\,\beta U(\mathbf{r}) = -a\beta \tag{28-9}$$

Thus, for temperatures greater than ϵ/k, $B(T)$ is indeed represented by

$$B(T) = b - \frac{a}{kT}, \tag{28-10}$$

and van der Waals' equation is expected to be reasonable.

In summary, the necessary and sufficient conditions for a second virial coefficient of the van der Walls type are the following: U(r)/kT *must be positive and much greater than unity for some range of* r, *and* U(r) *must be much less than* kT *over the rest of the range* (over most of which it will be negative).

Of course, in actual practice, the parameters a and b are chosen to give the best fit to the experimental data available. The equation has proved useful even at densities and temperatures for which it is theoretically unjustifiable. This is not surprising, since a good empirical equation is often useful in ranges of its variables well outside the limits of its theoretical justification.

PROBLEMS

28-1. For P-V-T work, the best two-parameter equation of state is probably the so-called *Dieterici equation*,

$$Pe^{Na/VkT}(V - Nb) = NkT.$$

What is the second virial coefficient for this equation?

28-2. Suppose the molecules were actually hard spheres. Interpret van der Waals' b in terms of the volume of a hard sphere molecule.

28-3. At the critical point, the P-V isotherm has an inflection point, characterized by $(\partial P/\partial V)_T = 0$ and $(\partial^2 P/\partial V^2)_T = 0$. Express the temperature, volume, and pressure of a system at the critical point, T_c, V_c, and P_c, for a van der Waals fluid in terms of van der Waals' a and b and the number of particles N.

28-4. For simplicity, equations of state are often expressed in terms of dimensionless (or reduced) variables T_R, V_R, and P_R, defined by

$$T_R = T/T_c; \quad V_R = V/V_c; \quad P_R = P/P_c.$$

Write the van der Waals equation in terms of dimensionless variables.

28-5. Suppose you wanted to extend the equation of state to lower temperatures by adding another parameter. What would you get if you just took one term more in the series expansion in Eq. 28-8?

28-6. Summarize the physical requirements which must be met for the van der Waals equation to be justifiable. Compare with the formulation of van der Waals' equation you will find in almost any book on physical chemistry.

29   PERFECT CRYSTALS

The mechanical picture of a perfect crystal is very much like that of a single, extremely large molecule. If it consists of a total of N atoms, the crystal is analogous to a huge molecule made up of N particles. Each of these particles is bound into the crystal lattice; therefore it has neither rotational nor free translational energy. The total internal energy of the crystal must lie in the contributions from the many vibrational modes of the particles.

Each particle in the crystal has three degrees of freedom; that is, specification of three coordinates is necessary to fix its position. Therefore, mechanically, the complete crystal has $3N$ degrees of freedom. Three of these are specified by fixing the center of mass of the crystal and three by orienting its axes in space. Associated with these six coordinates are the translational and rotational energy of the crystal as a whole. Such energies are easily handled by classical mechanics and do not normally hold statistical mechanical interest.

This leaves $3N - 6$ coordinates which may be specified independently to make the crystal a completely determined mechanical entity. These $3N - 6$ coordinates and their corresponding momenta are the phase space variables for the crystal. They should be chosen in such a way that the energies relating to them may be simply expressed. These energies are vibrational, and the choice of $3N - 6$ coordinates in which the vibrations may be taken to be simple harmonic is a major problem. These are called the *normal coordinates* of the crystal, in complete analogy to the normal coordinates for the vibrational modes in a molecule.

The normal coordinates are so chosen that associated with each one is an energy contribution of the form of a harmonic oscillator, Eq. 19-17:

$$\epsilon_i = (n_i + \tfrac{1}{2})\hbar\omega_i. \tag{29-1}$$

The characteristic angular velocity (sometimes called frequency) ω_i depends on the particular normal coordinate. There will be $3N - 6$ frequencies ω_i. The problem of how the characteristic frequencies of these normal modes of vibration are distributed is the primary problem in treating crystals by statistical mechanics. Each normal mode is independent of each other, so the energies given by Eq. 29-1 may be used in the partition function to find the desired thermodynamic variables. However, the question of the distribution of the frequencies ω_i for the $3N - 6$ normal modes is very complicated.

We shall carry the problem along formally as far as possible before worrying about the frequencies. The partition function is the sum over quantum states,

$$Q = \sum_{\text{states}} e^{-\beta E(\text{state})}. \tag{29-2}$$

In complete analogy to Sec. 19, Q factors into separate vibrational and electronic contributions. The electronic part is treated in the same way it was for gas molecules. In the interest of simplicity, the degeneracy of the electronic ground state of the constituent particles is taken as zero and Q_{elect} is unity. If this happened not to be the case, the change could be easily made. Furthermore, if there were free electrons in the crystal, as there are in metals, they would have to be treated separately in some fashion similar to that of Sec. 24. The treatment of this section would then be valid only for the lattice of ions in the metal.

The only energy, then, contributing to Eq. 29-2, is

$$E(\text{state}) = \sum_{i=1}^{3N} (n_i + \tfrac{1}{2})\hbar\omega_i. \tag{29-3}$$

In Eq. 29-3, $3N$ different normal modes are indicated rather than $3N - 6$. For macroscopic crystals, 6 is certainly negligible compared to $3N$. The sum over quantum states in Eq. 29-2 represents the independent summation over *each* vibrational quantum number n_i from zero to infinity. The summations are independent because the normal coordinates are so chosen that the vibrations have no effect on each other, at least for the lowest vibrational levels.

The particles comprising the crystal may well be indistinguishable, but this has no effect on Q. The partition function tells how the system energy is partitioned among the $6N$ different normal modes. The normal modes are completely distinguishable. They are all different, pertaining as they do to certain well-defined vibrational motions among the various mechanical parts of the crystal.

Since the energy, Eq. 29-3, is a sum, the partition function factorizes, as in the case of ideal gases:

$$Q = \left(\sum_{n_1=0}^{\infty} e^{-\beta(n_1+\frac{1}{2})\hbar\omega_1} \right) \left(\sum_{n_2=0}^{\infty} e^{-\beta(n_2+\frac{1}{2})\hbar\omega_2} \right) \cdots$$

$$= e^{-\beta\hbar(\omega_1+\omega_2+\cdots)/2} \left(\sum_{n_1=0}^{\infty} e^{-n_1\beta\hbar\omega_1} \right) \left(\sum_{n_2=0}^{\infty} e^{-n_2\beta\hbar\omega_2} \right) \cdots. \qquad (29\text{-}4)$$

The constant zero-point energies were taken outside the summations. The sums may be found using Eq. 19-21:

$$\sum_{n_i=0}^{\infty} e^{-n_i\beta\hbar\omega_i} = \frac{1}{1 - e^{-\beta\hbar\omega_i}}. \qquad (29\text{-}5)$$

Thus, Eq. 29-4 gives the logarithm of Q to be simply

$$\ln Q = - \sum_{i=1}^{3N} \frac{\hbar\omega_i}{2kT} - \sum_{j=1}^{3N} \ln (1 - e^{-\hbar\omega_j/kT}). \qquad (29\text{-}6)$$

From Eq. 29-6 and the equations of Sec. 11, all thermodynamic properties of a perfect crystal could be calculated if only the distribution of the normal frequencies ω_i were known. The bonds holding together a crystal lattice are less strong than most chemical bonds. As can be seen from Table 19-1, the forces of chemical bonds are so strong that vibrational frequencies are high enough to make $\hbar\omega = kT$ at temperatures of, say, $3000°K$ in a typical case. The weaker forces in a crystal typically give frequencies about ten times lower; thus $\hbar\omega = kT$ at about $300°K$.

The first choice of frequency "distribution" considered here is that proposed as an approximate treatment by Einstein in 1907:

$$\omega_i = \omega_E, \qquad \text{a constant for all } i. \qquad (29\text{-}7)$$

Einstein's theory proves to be all right at high temperatures and only qualitatively reasonable at low temperatures. Equation 29-7 would seem a respectable approximation for temperatures high enough that all vibrational modes are excited, because just how they came to be excited—one after another as the temperature increased—would then be of little importance. The use of an average frequency as representative of them all would not be too unreasonable. A physical model could be given by imagining each normal mode to be the vibration of one of the N particles about its equilibrium configuration. Each particle should experience a similar environmental potential energy, approximately the same in all three directions. Then all normal frequencies would be identical, but this is not a very sound model.

The results of Einstein's theory are certainly simple, however. If Eq. 29-7 is used to define a characteristic temperature Θ_E,

$$\hbar\omega_E = k\Theta_E, \tag{29-8}$$

then Eq. 29-6 becomes

$$\ln Q = -\frac{3N\Theta_E}{2T} - 3N \ln(1 - e^{-\Theta_E/T}). \tag{29-9}$$

All thermodynamic quantities of interest could be calculated from Eq. 29-9. In particular, the specific heat is interesting to compare with experiment:

$$\bar{E} = kT^2 \left(\frac{\partial \ln Q}{\partial T}\right)_{V,N_i} \tag{29-10}$$

$$= kT^2 \frac{3N\Theta_E}{2T^2} + kT^2 3N \frac{e^{-\Theta_E/T}\Theta_E}{(1 - e^{-\Theta_E/T})T^2},$$

$$\bar{E} = \tfrac{3}{2}Nk\Theta_E + \frac{3Nk\Theta_E}{e^{\Theta_E/T} - 1}; \tag{29-11}$$

$$\overline{C_V} = \left(\frac{\partial \bar{E}}{\partial T}\right)_{V,N_i} = 3Nk\left(\frac{\Theta_E}{T}\right)^2 \frac{e^{\Theta_E/T}}{(e^{\Theta_E/T} - 1)^2}. \tag{29-12}$$

The heat capacity of a crystal, according to Einstein's theory, is a universal function of Θ_E/T. The parameter Θ_E will, of course, vary from crystal to crystal. Experimentally, it is true that plots of heat capacity versus temperature do have similar shapes for monatomic crystals and may often be superimposed by proper scaling of the temperature. At high temperatures, Θ_E/T is small and Eq. 29-12 becomes

$$\overline{C_V} \to 3Nk, \qquad T \gg \Theta_E. \tag{29-13}$$

This has long been recognized experimentally as the law of *Dulong and Petit*. This is by no means an astonishing result, since it is just the classical limit of the contribution to heat capacity of N simple harmonic oscillators, as was discussed in Secs. 16 and 19. However, at low temperatures, where C_V is sensitive to the fraction of the normal modes which are excited, the limit of Eq. 29-12,

$$\overline{C_V} \to 3Nk\left(\frac{\Theta_E}{T}\right)^2 e^{-\Theta_E/T}, \qquad T \ll \Theta_E, \tag{29-14}$$

approaches zero too rapidly for decreasing T because of the damping of the exponential. This is to be expected for a model which gives the same characteristic temperature to all normal modes. It is very difficult to excite any of them at temperatures much below Θ_E. Thus, $\overline{C_V}$ would be low, because very little heat could raise the temperature considerably. Then, as T increases to Θ_E, $\overline{C_V}$ would rise rapidly and level off at $3Nk$. Such behavior is not observed physically.

Clearly, Einstein's choice of a single frequency, Eq. 29-7 is a gross oversimplification. Experimentally, it is known that for most crystals, C_V approaches zero as T^3. It is therefore reasonable to seek a distribution of normal frequencies which makes C_V approach zero as T^3 for low temperatures and approach the Dulong and Petit value $3Nk$ for high temperatures. A physically reasonable interpolation between these limits was developed by Debye in 1912. It has proved very useful in correlating theory with experiment.

The Debye theory asks the question, what are the normal modes of vibration which have *low frequencies*, that is, have long wave length? The answer is, they should be directly analogous to the vibrations in a crystal by which sound waves are transmitted. If they are assumed to be identical, then the frequency distribution of these vibrational modes has already been found in Eqs. 25-4 to 25-15. It was shown there that if waves propagate within a volume V at speed c, the number of quantum states with frequencies between ω and $\omega + d\omega$ is

$$\frac{V\omega^2 \, d\omega}{2\pi^2 c^3} . \tag{29-15}$$

For vibrations in a lattice there are three possible polarizations, two transverse waves at right angles to each other and one longitudinal (in contrast to sound waves, which have only the longitudinal). So for lattice vibrations in a crystal of volume V, the number of quantum states or normal modes of vibration with frequencies between ω and $\omega + d\omega$ is

$$\frac{V\omega^2 \, d\omega}{2\pi^2} \left(\frac{1}{c_{1,\text{trans}}^3} + \frac{1}{c_{2,\text{trans}}^3} + \frac{1}{c_{\text{long}}^3} \right) \tag{29-16}$$

The sum in the parenthesis is a property of the crystal and is often written in terms of an average speed of sound in the crystal $\bar{c}$, defined by

$$\frac{3}{\bar{c}^3} \equiv \frac{1}{c_{1,\text{trans}}^3} + \frac{1}{c_{2,\text{trans}}^3} + \frac{1}{c_{\text{long}}^3} . \tag{29-17}$$

In this notation, the number of independent normal modes in a crystal of volume V whose characteristic frequencies lie between ω and $\omega + d\omega$ is

$$\frac{3V\omega^2\,d\omega}{2\pi^2\bar{c}^3}. \tag{29-18}$$

Once Eq. 29-18 is adopted for the frequency distribution, the partition function, Eq. 29-6, immediately gives the thermodynamic variables. Only one last item of importance remains—to cut off the total number of normal modes at $3N$. Clearly, there are only enough degrees of freedom in the crystal to allow $3N$ normal modes. The usual choice is the set of $3N$ modes of the same form as the $3N$ sound waves of longest wave length which may be propagated through the crystal. Thus, any frequency is prohibited that is greater than $\omega_{\max}$, defined by equating the sum of all modes with $\omega < \omega_{\max}$ to $3N$,

$$\int_0^{\omega_{\max}} \frac{3V\omega^2\,d\omega}{2\pi^2\bar{c}^3} = 3N. \tag{29-19}$$

The frequency of the Debye cutoff, called the **Debye frequency**, is found by integration of Eq. 29-19:

$$\frac{V\omega_{\max}^3}{2\pi^2\bar{c}^3} = 3N; \qquad \omega_{\max} = \bar{c}\left(\frac{6\pi^2 N}{V}\right)^{\frac{1}{3}}. \tag{29-20}$$

The cutoff frequency may be thought of as defining the so-called **Debye characteristic temperature** Θ_D:

$$k\Theta_D = \hbar\omega_{\max}, \tag{29-21}$$

in terms of which some of the results appear simpler. The Debye temperature is a function of both $\bar{c}$ and N/V.

In Fig. 29-1, plots of the frequency distribution of normal modes in a crystal are shown for both the Einstein and the Debye theories. The area under either curve between any two values of ω is the number of vibrational quantum states in the crystal with frequency between the two values, according to the appropriate theory. The total area under each curve is of course $3N$. Clearly there could be any number of other choices of the frequency distribution. Much theoretical work has gone into finding more nearly exact distributions, but the results have been both complicated and disappointing.*

* For references and a brief discussion, see Hill, Sec. 5-4. However, the general reference to the entire subject of heat capacities of solids is M. Blackman, *Handbuch der Physik* (Springer, Berlin) **7.1**, 325 (1955), which is the source of the numerical data given in Table 29-1.

In order to replace the summations over states in Eq. 29-6 by integrations over ω, Eq. 29-6 must be multiplied by the number of states between ω and $\omega + d\omega$ as given by Eq. 29-18:

$$\ln Q = -\int_0^{\omega_{max}} \left(\frac{\hbar\omega}{2kT}\right)\left(\frac{3V\omega^2\,d\omega}{2\pi^2\bar{c}^3}\right)$$

$$-\int_0^{\omega_{max}} \ln\left(1 - e^{-\hbar\omega/kT}\right)\frac{3V\omega^2\,d\omega}{2\pi^2\bar{c}^3}. \tag{29-22}$$

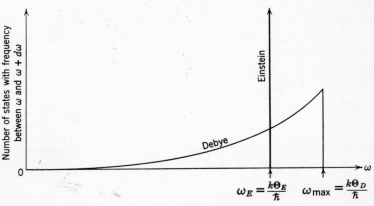

Fig. 29-1. Frequency distributions of normal modes in crystals for Einstein and Debye theories.

The variable change $z = \hbar\omega/kT$ is customarily made in the last term. The logarithm of the partition function is written below in two equivalent forms:

$$\ln Q = -\frac{3V\hbar\omega_{max}^4}{16\pi^2kT\bar{c}^3} - \frac{3Vk^3T^3}{2\pi^2\bar{c}^3\hbar^3}\int_0^{\Theta_D/T} \ln\left(1 - e^{-z}\right)z^2\,dz; \tag{29-23}$$

$$\ln Q = -\frac{9N\Theta_D}{8T} - 3N\ln\left(1 - e^{-\Theta_D/T}\right) + \frac{3NT^3}{\Theta_D^3}\int_0^{\Theta_D/T} \frac{z^3\,dz}{e^z - 1}. \tag{29-24}$$

All thermodynamic properties of an ideal crystal may be calculated as functions of Θ_D from Eq. 29-23 or 29-24. Sometimes Eqs. B-10 and B-11 are utilized; and some results are expressible in terms of the so-called **Debye function** $D(x)$, a tabulated function* which is defined by

$$D(x) = \frac{3}{x^3}\int_0^x \frac{z^3\,dz}{e^z - 1}. \tag{29-25}$$

* G. N. Lewis, M. Randall, K. S. Pitzer, and L. Brewer, *Thermodynamics*, McGraw-Hill Book Company, New York, 1961, pp. 659–664.

A few results are compiled below:

$$\bar{E} = \tfrac{9}{8}Nk\Theta_D + 3NkTD\left(\frac{\Theta_D}{T}\right); \tag{29-26}$$

$$\bar{C}_v = 3Nk\left[4D\left(\frac{\Theta_D}{T}\right) - \frac{3(\Theta_D/T)}{e^{\Theta_D/T} - 1)}\right]; \tag{29-27}$$

$$\bar{S} = 3Nk\left[\tfrac{4}{3}D\left(\frac{\Theta_D}{T}\right) - \ln\left(1 - e^{-\Theta_D/T}\right)\right]. \tag{29-28}$$

Values of Θ_D have been chosen for various crystals to give the best fit to the experimental heat capacity curves. Because the theory is not exact, different values of Θ_D enable different parts of the heat capacity curves to be fit. Values of Θ_D are tabulated in Table 29-1 in the form of the

Table 29-1. Partial Periodic Table of the Elements, Showing the Characteristic Debye Temperature Θ_D in Degrees Kelvin if Available

Li	Be											B	C	N	O
430	980												1860		
Na	Mg											Al	Si	P	S
160	330											380			
K	Ca	Sc	Ti	V	Cr	Mn	Fe	Co	Ni	Cu	Zn	Ga	Ge	As	Se
99	230				405		433	445	456	310	240		362		
Rb	Sr	Y	Zr	Nb	Mo	Tc	Ru	Rn	Pd	Ag	Cd	In	Sn	Sb	Te
					375					220	165		165	204	
Cs	Ba		Hf	Ta	W	Re	Os	Ir	Pt	Au	Hg	Tl	Pb	Bi	Po
					315				225	185	90		86	111	

Most data taken from Blackman, *Handbuch der Physik*, **7.1**, 325 (1955).
Carbon is given for the diamond form.

periodic table, which brings out certain trends. In changing from one element to another, both the interatomic potential and the atomic mass are altered. Both effects change the frequency distribution of normal modes. The most obvious trend is that heavier elements in a given period have a denser distribution of vibrational states; thus ω_{max} and Θ_D decrease going down the periodic table, and the classical Dulong and Petit behavior extends down to lower temperatures. This behavior is qualitatively reasonable, viewed from the classical theory of simple harmonic motion in elementary physics. This gives the frequency of vibration as proportional to $\sqrt{K/m}$, where K is the force constant and m the mass. As the frequencies are decreased, so is Θ_D.

In Fig. 29-2, heat capacity as calculated from the Debye theory is plotted versus temperature. It has both the Dulong and Petit limiting value for high temperatures and T^3 dependence for low temperatures,

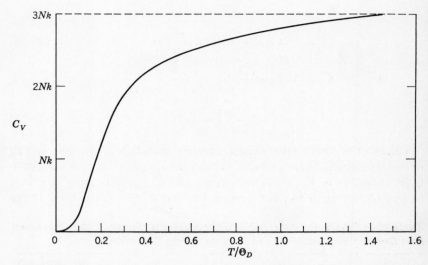

Fig. 29-2. Plot of C_V versus temperature, as calculated from the Debye theory.

as the reader will verify in the problems. Both in the T^3 region and in the interpolation region the Debye theory agrees well with experiment for many crystals.

PROBLEMS

29-1. Find $\bar{C}_V$ in the limit of very low temperature (Debye theory).

29-2. Prove the high temperature limit of $\bar{C}_V$, Eq. 29-27, is $3Nk$.

29-3. Calculate the coefficient of thermal expansion

$$\alpha = \frac{1}{V}\left(\frac{\partial V}{\partial T}\right)_P$$

for a Debye solid. What is its high temperature limit?

30   EQUILIBRIUM CONSTANTS

This section treats the calculation of equilibrium constants for chemical reactions by means of the partition function. Sometimes these constants may be calculated more accurately then they may be measured.

BASIC EQUATION OF CHEMICAL EQUILIBRIUM

In order to discuss all chemical reactions, a general way must be found to write the reaction. As an example, the chemical reaction

$$H_2 + Cl_2 \rightleftharpoons 2HCl$$

may be written

$$0 = 2HCl - H_2 - Cl_2.$$

This may be done for the expression of any chemical equilibrium, the general case being written

$$0 = \sum_i \nu_i A_i. \tag{30-1}$$

The A's are the chemical species: HCl, H_2, Cl_2, etc.; and the ν's are the stoichiometric numbers: positive for products and negative for reactants.

In thermodynamic treatments of chemical equilibrium, the basic equation is the following, which holds in the equilibrium mixture:

$$\sum_i \nu_i \mu_i = 0, \tag{30-2}$$

where μ_i is the chemical potential *per molecule* of species i. Chemists usually use μ_i as the chemical potential per *mole*, or partial molar Gibbs free energy, which is Avogadro's number times the μ_i used in this book. The thermodynamic proof of Eq. 30-2 is a consequence of that part of the second law which expresses the equilibrium condition as given by an extremum of a function of state, holding appropriate variables constant.

On the other hand, the statistical mechanical proof of Eq. 30-2 is immediate once the chemical potentials are related to the partition function. This is done in Sec. 11:

$$\bar{\mu}_i = \left(\frac{\partial \bar{A}}{\partial N_i}\right)_{T,V,N_{j \neq i}} = -kT\left(\frac{\partial \ln Q}{\partial N_i}\right)_{T,V,N_{j \neq i}} \tag{30-3}$$

The statistical mechanical formulation of the left-hand side of Eq. 30-2 is

$$\sum_i \nu_i \bar{\mu}_i = -\frac{kT}{Q} \sum_i \nu_i \left(\frac{\partial Q}{\partial N_i}\right)_{T,V,N_{j \neq i}}. \tag{30-4}$$

By its definition, Q is the summation,

$$Q = \sum_{\text{states}} e^{-\beta E(\text{state})}, \tag{30-5}$$

over *all possible* quantum states *for the equilibrium mixture*. It depends only on the temperature and on the set of energy levels for the available quantum states. This latter depends on the volume through its effect on the energy level of each state.

The question raised by Eq. 30-4 is whether or not

$$\sum_i \nu_i \left(\frac{\partial Q}{\partial N_i}\right)_{T,V,N_{j \neq i}} \tag{30-6}$$

vanishes. Since $\partial Q/\partial N_i$ is the change in Q caused by increasing by one the number of particles of type i, the expression in Eq. 30-6 represents the change in Q caused by altering *each* N_i by the stoichiometric number for species i. The complete set of quantum states used to obtain Q already contains states representing *every possible* set of the N_i which may be reached from any other by successive reactions of molecules according to the stoichiometric equation, 30-1. Thus, the complete set of quantum states does not change when acted on by $\sum_i \nu_i(\partial/\partial N_i)$, and the right-hand side of Eq. 30-4 is zero.

This result is completely analogous to the equilibrium relation found for photons in Eq. 25-1, $\bar{\mu} = 0$. It arose there because any number of photons could be created or destroyed at the walls of the enclosure; thus states representing all possible numbers were included in Q. For chemical reactions, particles are created and destroyed only in accordance with the stoichiometric equation, 30-1, so Q must contain all states for occupation numbers so related.

As an example, suppose one starts the HCl synthesis with 500 H_2 molecules and 500 Cl_2 molecules. Then not only must all quantum states for a 500-500 mixture be contained in Q, but the quantum states for all other sets of N_i given by the rows of Table 30-1 must also be included. The numbers of particles of the various species are unknown. All that is known is that whatever they are, they must be obtainable from a 500-500 mixture by successive reactions according to the stoichiometry. All possibilities have their probabilities given by the ensemble, so Q contains them all. It is clear that the operation of $\Sigma_i \, \nu_i(\partial/\partial N_i)$ on the terms in Q

Table 30-1. Various Sets of N_i Included in Q for an Equilibrium Mixture Initially Composed of 500 H_2 Molecules and 500 Cl_2 Molecules

No. of H_2 molecules	No. of Cl_2 molecules	No. of HCl molecules
500	500	0
499	499	2
498	498	4
497	497	6
496	496	8
.	.	.
.	.	.
.	.	.

from each row of Table 30-1 merely transforms those terms into the ones in the next row down. For large N's one need not worry about what happens in the last row. Clearly, there is *no* dependence in Q on occupation number changes linked by the stoichiometric numbers as in Eq. 30-6. The statistical mechanical equivalent of Eq. 30-2 has therefore been demonstrated:

$$\boxed{\sum_i \nu_i \bar{\mu}_i = 0.}$$

(30-7)

This is the basic equation of chemical equilibrium.

Clearly, statistical mechanics will not be able to say which row in Table 30-1 represents the system. The hope is, however, that the ensemble *average* of the number of H_2 molecules, say, will be representative of the number actually found. The problem of how good a representation this average is is discussed in Sec. 33. It is seen there that for the enormous number of particles in macroscopic systems, significant departures from the ensemble averages are extremely unlikely.

ACTIVITIES AND THE EQUILIBRIUM CONSTANT

In the equilibrium mixture, the chemical potentials in general are functions of the concentrations of the various species, the environment of the molecules, and all kinds of other things. One may put all this complexity into a single defined quantity a_i, the activity of substance i. This is done by first choosing arbitrarily a reference condition or **standard state** for substance i whose chemical potential if it were in that physical condition would be $\mu_i{}^0$. In general, $\mu_i{}^0$ depends on the conditions chosen to determine the reference state, in particular on the temperature and pressure.* The **activity** of substance i, a_i, in the equilibrium mixture is then defined by the equation

$$\boxed{\bar{\mu}_i = \bar{\mu}_i{}^0 + kT \ln \bar{a}_i.}$$
(30-8)

Note that the chemical potential μ_i in the equilibrium mixture is determined by nature. Once the standard state is chosen, $\mu_i{}^0$ is also so determined. The activity, then, is just the function of the thermodynamic variables that makes Eq. 30-8 valid, regardless of how complicated a function this may demand it to be.

Use of Eq. 30-8 in Eq. 30-7 immediately gives an expression for the equilibrium constant:

$$\sum_i \nu_i \bar{\mu}_i{}^0 + kT \sum_i \nu_i \ln \bar{a}_i = 0,$$
(30-9)

$$\sum_i \nu_i \bar{\mu}_i{}^0 = -kT \ln (\bar{a}_1{}^{\nu_1} \cdot \bar{a}_2{}^{\nu_2} \cdot \bar{a}_3{}^{\nu_3} \cdots),$$

$$\boxed{\Delta \bar{\mu}^0 = -kT \ln \bar{K}_{\text{eq}}.}$$
(30-10)

This important equation is familiar from thermodynamics. The two quantities $\Delta \bar{\mu}^0$ and $\bar{K}_{\text{eq}}$ are defined by

$$\Delta \bar{\mu}^0 = \sum_i \nu_i \bar{\mu}_i{}^0$$
(30-11)

and

$$\bar{K}_{\text{eq}} = \bar{a}_1{}^{\nu_1} \cdot \bar{a}_2{}^{\nu_2} \cdot \bar{a}_3{}^{\nu_3} \cdots.$$
(30-12)

The first is clearly the sum of the $\mu_i{}^0$ for each product molecule minus the same sum for each reactant molecule. The second is the familiar equilibrium constant, expressed in terms of activities.

* These are discussed in most thermodynamics books. See especially G. N. Lewis, M. Randall, K. S. Pitzer, and L. Brewer, *Thermodynamics*, McGraw-Hill Book Co., New York, 2d ed., 1961, Chap. 20.

In statistical mechanics, the equilibrium constant in terms of activities is obtained directly from the chemical potentials of the pure reactants and the pure products in their standard conditions. The energies of the various quantum states for the reactant and product molecules which are needed to find the partition functions may often be found from spectroscopic studies and a knowledge of quantum mechanics. This is briefly treated in Sec. 32. Given the partition function, the $\bar{\mu}^{0}$'s and thus $\overline{K_{eq}}$ may be calculated directly.

Clearly, some consistent choice for the zero of energy must be made for all reactant and product molecules in forming the partition functions. The usual choice is to assign zero energy to either the reactants or the products when the molecules are decomposed into atoms and the atoms are a long way from each other and have no kinetic energy. Obviously, this is the same for both reactants and products, since both contain the same atoms. Of course, using this convention, stable configurations of atoms in molecules may have *negative* energy relative to the zero, but this should cause no alarm.

It is usually not hard to calculate $\overline{K_{eq}}$ from the partition functions of the reactants and products in their standard conditions. This is because the standard conditions may be defined at will, and nothing prevents their being chosen so that the $\bar{\mu}^{0}$'s are easily found. If a gas is involved, its standard condition may be set as one atmosphere pressure and hypothetical *ideal* condition. Whether the gas actually exhibits ideal behavior at one atmosphere pressure is immaterial. One may imagine its existence and use this as the defined standard condition. For such a gas, $\bar{\mu}^0$ is easily calculated. Similarly, the standard conditions of crystals and solutions are generally chosen with the simple calculation of the $\bar{\mu}^{0}$'s in view.

Once $\overline{K_{eq}}$ has been found, a problem still remains. The equilibrium constant is given in terms of activities, which are not directly measurable, but are only defined by Eq. 30-8. The results of physical measurements are values of, say, the pressure, density, or mole fraction. Activities are not measured directly. The equilibrium constant given for activities must be expressed in terms of these observable quantities if it is to help predict experimental results. It is here that statistical mechanics bogs down in difficulties for cases in which the final equilibrium condition is neither an ideal mixture of gases nor an ideal solution. Because of these difficulties, the relationship between activities and pressure or concentration in the equilibrium system is customarily obtained empirically. For this reason, as a starting point, the ideal gas result, discussed below, is very important.

EQUILIBRIUM IN AN IDEAL GAS

In an ideal mixture of ideal gases, the gas molecules exist in the confining volume completely unaware of the fact that other species are present. For this reason, the chemical potential of a constituent of an ideal gas mixture depends on the density of the particular species and in no way on the other species which might be present. The $\overline{\mu}_{i,\ \text{ideal gas}}$ calculated from the partition function for a mixture will therefore be the same as that for the pure gas. A simple extension of Prob. 20-5 shows that for an ideal mixture of ideal gases

$$Q_{\text{ideal mixture}} = \frac{1}{N_1!}\, q_1{}^{N_1} \cdot \frac{1}{N_2!}\, q_2{}^{N_2} \cdot \frac{1}{N_3!}\, q_3{}^{N_3} \cdots . \tag{30-13}$$

On using Stirling's formula, Eq. 20-3,

$$\ln Q_{\text{ideal mixture}} = N_1 \ln \frac{eq_1}{N_1} + N_2 \ln \frac{eq_2}{N_2} + \cdots . \tag{30-14}$$

Thus, for the ith component of an ideal mixture of ideal gases,

$$\overline{\mu}_{i,\ \text{ideal gas}} = -kT\left(\frac{\partial \ln Q}{\partial N_i}\right)_{T,V,N_j \neq i} \tag{30-15}$$

$$= -kT \ln \frac{eq_i}{N_i} + kT,$$

$$\boxed{\overline{\mu}_{i,\ \text{ideal gas}} = -kT \ln \frac{q_i}{N_i}.} \tag{30-16}$$

Equation 30-16 holds for either a pure ideal gas or for the ith component of an ideal mixture of ideal gases.

The definition of the standard condition for an ideal gas contained in a volume V and at temperature T is equivalent merely to picking a number $N_i{}^0$ of molecules of type i which are in the volume when the standard condition is realized. Generally, $N_i{}^0$ is selected by the criterion of demanding one atmosphere pressure at the standard condition:

$$P_i{}^0 = \frac{N_i{}^0 kT}{V} = 1 \text{ atm} \tag{30-17}$$

or

$$N_i{}^0 = \frac{(1 \text{ atm})V}{kT}, \tag{30-18}$$

in which case $N_i{}^0$ would be the same for all components.

Combining Eq. 30-16 with Eq. 30-10 gives $\overline{K_{\text{eq}}}$ for ideal gas reactions:

$$\sum_i \nu_i \overline{\mu}_i^0 = -kT \ln \overline{K_{\text{eq}}};$$ (30-19)

$$-kT \sum_i \nu_i \ln \frac{q_i}{N_i^0} = -kT \ln \overline{K_{\text{eq}}};$$ (30-20)

$$\overline{K_{\text{eq}}} = \left(\frac{q_1}{N_1^0}\right)^{\nu_1} \cdot \left(\frac{q_2}{N_2^0}\right)^{\nu_2} \cdot \left(\frac{q_3}{N_3^0}\right)^{\nu_3} \cdots.$$ (30-21)

With Eq. 30-21 the first problem of chemical equilibrium has been solved, that is, to express $\overline{K_{\text{eq}}}$ in terms of Q. This equilibrium constant is in terms of activities, which are defined by Eq. 30-8.

The second problem is to express the activity in terms of some measurable quantity. The solution of this problem is easy for an ideal gas. The expression for $\overline{\mu}_i$, Eq. 30-16, may be cast into the form of Eq. 30-8 directly:

$$\overline{\mu}_{i,\,\text{ideal gas}} = -kT \ln \frac{q_i}{N_i}$$ (30-22)

$$= -kT \ln \left(\frac{q_i}{N_i^0} \cdot \frac{N_i^0}{N_i}\right)$$

$$= -kT \ln \frac{q_i}{N_i^0} + kT \ln \frac{N_i}{N_i^0}$$

$$= \overline{\mu}_{i,\,\text{ideal gas}}^0 + kT \ln \overline{a}_{i,\,\text{ideal gas}}.$$ (30-23)

This is of the correct form, and the activity of an ideal gas is simply

$$\overline{a}_{i,\,\text{ideal gas}} = \frac{N_i}{N_i^0}.$$ (30-24)

One sometimes sees Eq. 30-24 combined with the conventional choice of N_i°, Eq. 30-18:

$$\overline{a}_{i,\,\text{ideal gas}} = \frac{\overline{N}_i kT}{(1\text{ atm})V} = \frac{\overline{P}_i}{1\text{ atm}},$$ (30-25)

which illustrates the well-known fact that the activity of an ideal gas is simply proportional to its pressure.

A simple and intuitive result is obtained by starting with the definition of the equilibrium constant,

$$\overline{K}_{\text{eq, ideal gas}} = \overline{a}_1^{\nu_1} \cdot \overline{a}_2^{\nu_2} \cdot \overline{a}_3^{\nu_3} \cdots,$$ (30-26)

and substituting from Eq. 30-21 on the left-hand side and Eq. 30-24 on the right:

$$\left(\frac{q_1}{N_1{}^0}\right)^{\nu_1} \cdot \left(\frac{q_2}{N_2{}^0}\right)^{\nu_2} \cdots = \left(\frac{\overline{N_1}}{N_1{}^0}\right)^{\nu_1} \cdot \left(\frac{\overline{N_2}}{N_2{}^0}\right)^{\nu_2} \cdots. \tag{30-27}$$

Thus, for equilibria in ideal gases,

$$\boxed{\overline{N_1}^{\nu_1} \cdot \overline{N_2}^{\nu_2} \cdot \overline{N_3}^{\nu_3} \cdots = q_1{}^{\nu_1} \cdot q_2{}^{\nu_2} \cdot q_3{}^{\nu_3} \cdots.} \tag{30-28}$$

Equation 30-28 is discussed in the next paragraph. It is convenient here to note that the ideal gas law may be used to obtain $\overline{K_P}$ instead of the ratios of the numbers of molecules:

$$\left(\frac{\overline{P_1}V}{kT}\right)^{\nu_1} \cdot \left(\frac{\overline{P_2}V}{kT}\right)^{\nu_2} \cdot \left(\frac{\overline{P_3}V}{kT}\right)^{\nu_3} \cdots = q_1{}^{\nu_1}q_2{}^{\nu_2}q_3{}^{\nu_3} \cdots, \tag{30-29}$$

$$\overline{K_P} = q_1{}^{\nu_1}q_2{}^{\nu_2}q_3{}^{\nu_3} \cdots \left(\frac{kT}{V}\right)^{\Delta\nu}. \tag{30-30}$$

The other useful equilibrium constants, such as those for concentrations, mole fractions, or densities, may be similarly obtained.

DISCUSSION

The simplicity of Eq. 30-28 is striking. In the idealized chemical reaction (an isomeric equilibrium, for example),

$$A \rightleftharpoons B, \tag{30-31}$$

one has simply

$$\frac{\overline{N_B}}{\overline{N_A}} = \frac{\displaystyle\sum_{\text{states of } B} e^{-\epsilon(\text{state})/kT}}{\displaystyle\sum_{\text{states of } A} e^{-\epsilon(\text{state})/kT}}. \tag{30-32}$$

Those products or reactants are favored which have relatively large values of q at the temperatures in question. Large values of q may arise in two ways. Individual terms in the sum over states may be large because the species has *low lying energy levels*. Also, many small terms may make q large because there exist a *great many states* whose energies lie in a small range.

The low lying levels are particularly important at low temperatures, since only low levels are populated when T is small. The effect of a high density of states will be damped at low temperatures by the exponential. But as the temperature is increased, the exponential distribution becomes more uniform, and species with a high density of states begin to predominate. This latter effect is one of increased entropy—loss of specific information about the state the system is in as a great many states become about equally populated.

The chemical equilibrium is thus seen as a balance between the effects of energy and of entropy, even on the microscopic scale. In macroscopic thermodynamics this is observed in the recognition that it is the change in the quantity $H - TS$ which governs the reaction equilibrium. It is not the heat of reaction or the entropy change alone.

In gas reactions more complicated than Eq. 30-31, the same qualitative features hold. For a reaction with more product molecules than reactant, the entropy effect appears clearly in their being more q's in the numerator than denominator of Eq. 30-28. At temperatures for which a great many levels are thawed out for all the species, just this fact of the number of q's governs the size of Eq. 30-28. At low temperatures, the species with especially low energies are favored.

For real mixtures at equilibrium, the physical picture is similar, but the mathematics more difficult. In that case, the intermolecular potential contributions to the total energy couple each species to each other. The equilibrium constant, Eq. 30-10, is no harder, because of the choice of standard states. However, in order to relate the activities in $\overline{K}_{eq}$ to experimental quantities like pressures and concentrations, the chemical potentials of the various species must be found from the real partition function for the mixture by Eq. 30-3. In general, this will be a complicated function of concentration. Then Eq. 30-8 gives the activity,

$$\overline{a}_i = e^{(\overline{\mu}_i - \overline{\mu}_i{}^0)/kT}. \tag{30-33}$$

Activities of the form of Eq. 30-33 are then substituted into the $\overline{K}_{eq}$ of Eq. 30-10.

Clearly, for equilibrium systems which are not ideal mixtures or else involve perfect crystals, the statistical mechanics is difficult at best. But for many cases in which ideal conditions are approximated, equilibrium constants calculated by statistical mechanics from the known energy levels of the molecules are more precise than even the best experimental measurements.

PROBLEMS

30-1. For the general ideal gas reaction, Eq. 30-7, write the equivalent of Eq. 30-28 for the particle *densities* ρ_i instead of for the N_i.

30-2. Express the equilibrium constant for particle densities for the ideal gas reaction $AB \rightleftharpoons A + B$ in terms of the atomic masses m_A and m_B, the characteristic temperatures for the AB molecule Θ_{rot} and Θ_{vib}, the ground state degeneracies $g_{0,A}$, $g_{0,B}$, and $g_{0,AB}$, and D_0 for the AB molecule. Be sure to use the same zero of energy for q_{AB} as for q_A and q_B. At temperatures well below Θ_{vib}, how does the equilibrium constant change with increasing T? For *very* high temperatures, what temperature dependence does your equation give? If this seems nonsensical, what assumption made in its derivation has broken down?

30-3. Contrast the result of Prob. 30-2 with what would be found for the reaction $A_2 \rightleftharpoons 2A$.

30-4. Express the equilibrium constant for particle densities for the ionization of a monatomic gas, $A \rightleftharpoons A^+ + e^-$. Assume no potential energy of interaction between the separated A^+ and e^-. The degeneracies of the three species are $g_{0,A}$, g_{0,A^+}, and 2 respectively. Consider only the ground electronic state of the A atom, the ionization energy for which is ϵ^0.

30-5. In the ionization treated in Prob. 30-4, define the temperature Θ_{ion} by the equation $\epsilon^0 = k\Theta_{ion}$. Estimate the value of T/Θ_{ion} at which the equilibrium constant has all three densities identical and with reasonable values, say, $10^{20}/cm^3$ The g_0's may be set equal to unity. A typical ionization energy is 12 ev, and 1 ev $= 1.6 \times 10^{-12}$ erg. A mole of electrons weighs about $\frac{1}{1840}$ g.

30-6. The energy required to ionize the hydrogen atom, $H \rightleftharpoons H^+ + e^-$, is 13.53 ev. The atom is doubly degenerate, but the ion has $g_0 = 1$. If an initial concentration of hydrogen atoms of 0.01 mole/liter is heated to 10,000°K, what fraction of atoms are ionized? Assume the fraction ionized is much less than unity.

30-7. Using data from Fig. 19-1, calculate the equilibrium constant in terms of densities for the ideal gas reaction, $H_2 + Cl_2 \rightleftharpoons 2HCl$, at 800°C. All species are singly degenerate.

30-8. Prove Eq. 30-16 directly from Eq. 23-12 without using Stirling's formula.

31 GASES—COMPLICATIONS IN PARTITION FUNCTION

In order to concentrate on the principles of statistical mechanics, we have so far treated especially simple models of molecules. The technicalities of complicated statistical thermodynamic calculations may be studied in the many books which emphasize applications.* Several of the more important complications which often arise are briefly discussed in this section.

* Davidson, Fowler and Guggenheim, Hill, Mayer and Mayer.

NON-IDEALITY

The complications introduced into the partition functions from considering molecular interactions were discussed in Secs. 26 to 28. Calculations of the second and higher virial coefficients have been made for various hypothetical intermolecular potentials, but they are invariably complicated. However, if a person is interested simply in knowing what corrections the molecular interactions make in the pressure, energy, or entropy of a fluid, he need not worry about the complicated calculations of statistical mechanics. This information may be obtained from empirical charts and tables.* These may be viewed as having the following basis in theory.

Imagine the following calculation: First, one represents the potential energy curve for interaction of two molecules, Fig. 12-1, by an analytic function of roughly the proper shape having three adjustable parameters a, b, and c. With this many parameters, one would hope to be able to fit the data very closely. Next, using this interaction potential, one integrates Eq. 26-15 to get the configurational contribution to the partition function. From the partition function, one obtains the equation of state and all other thermodynamic variables of interest. However, they are all expressed in terms of the parameters a, b, and c which describe the intermolecular potential. One wants to replace a, b, and c where they appear in the partition function by properties of the system that can be measured experimentally. Two of the three critical properties P_c, V_c, and T_c may be used, but only two. The three are not independent, since they are coupled by the equation of state. From the equation of state, by the method of Prob. 28-3, P_c, V_c, and T_c may be found. Choice of a third independent quantity is arbitrary, and the merits of several have been debated. For ease in visualizing extent of non-ideality, the equation of state may always be represented by

$$PV = zNkT, \tag{31-1}$$

where z is a function of state called the *compressibility factor*. Departures of z from unity clearly reflect non-ideal behavior. The critical state defines the so-called *critical compressibility factor* z_c, which is a

---

* G. N. Lewis, M. Randall, K. S. Pitzer, and L. Brewer, *Thermodynamics*, McGraw-Hill Book Co., New York, 1961, 2d ed., Appendix 1. Also, O. A. Hougen, K. M. Watson, and R. A. Ragatz, *Chemical Process Principles: Part II, Thermodynamics*, John Wiley and Sons, New York, 2d ed., 1959, Chap. 14.

convenient choice of a third independent quantity:

$$z_c = \frac{P_c V_c}{N k T_c}.$$ (31-2)

One only has to solve for a, b, and c in terms of P_c, T_c, and z_c and substitute into Q_{config}. This is similar to Prob. 28-4. From here, one is able to express the configurational contribution to any thermodynamic quantity in terms of the three experimental constants. In particular, deviations from the ideal gas law may be expressed in terms of the compressibility factor, which now is a function of P, T, P_c, T_c, and z_c. In order for z to be dimensionless, this function must be of the form

$$z = z\left(\frac{P}{P_c}, \frac{T}{T_c}, z_c\right) = z(P_R, T_R, z_c).$$ (31-3)

Thus, so long as the intermolecular potential may be expressed by a three-parameter function, z is a universal function for *all fluids* of the reduced pressure and temperature and of z_c. This is a generalization of the so-called **law of corresponding states**. Note, it is true in Prob. 28-4 without even involving z_c. This is because there one starts with an equation of state, van der Waals', which has only two adjustable parameters.

Based on extensive P-V-T data for many different fluids, Hougen, Watson, and Ragatz have tabulated z as a function of P_R, T_R, and z_c.* Furthermore, once this was done, they used thermodynamic equations to express the contribution of intermolecular potential energy to the molar enthalpy, energy, and entropy. These they also tabulated as departures from the values the respective functions would take if the fluid were an ideal gas. The results are simplified by the fact that z_c lies between 0.20 and 0.30 for almost all fluids.

This is a very pragmatic approach, one which is extremely useful and which bypasses the extraordinary difficulties of the statistical mechanical calculations. Most theoreticians would claim it was not very satisfying. The theoretician would prefer to go ahead and calculate Q_{config} exactly in terms of a, b, and c. He then would have the contributions to all thermodynamic variables due to the non-ideality of the fluid. He would still have to fit the parameters a, b, and c to the experimental data. Any three independent experimental results would serve to do this. He might well choose data which enabled his equations to fit actual behavior better than those of Hougen, Watson, and Ragatz. Of course, if he happened to choose

---

* Choices of third parameters other than z_c have also been made. Lewis, Randall, Pitzer, and Brewer use the so-called *acentric factor*, which is related to the slope of the vapor pressure versus temperature curve. This choice has certain advantages over Hougen, Watson, and Ragatz's use of z_c.

P_c, T_c, and z_c, then his results would be almost identical to theirs. He would, however, have *predicted* the shapes of all the various curves, while they were forced to find many of theirs from experimental data.

INTERNAL ROTATION

As mentioned in Sec. 19, the analysis of the $3n - 5$ or $3n - 6$ independent vibrational motions of a polyatomic molecule is often complicated. For some molecules, one of the motions corresponds to rotation of two parts of the molecule with respect to each other about the single bond joining the parts. The classic example is ethane, whose two methyl groups can rotate about the bond: $H_3C—CH_3$. Because organic chemists knew that rotation about this bond was rapid compared to macroscopic times of measurement, statistical mechanicians originally replaced the vibrational contribution to the partition function from this mode by a classical rotational contribution,

$$q_{\text{int rot}} = \frac{2I_r kT}{\sigma \hbar^2}. \qquad (31\text{-}4)$$

In Eq. 31-4, I_r is the *reduced moment of inertia* characterizing the internal rotation* and σ the symmetry number for the internal rotation. In the case of ethane, σ is 3. The symmetry number is discussed later in this section.

As it became possible to compare accurate experimental results with the theory, discrepancies arose. The entropy calculated using Eq. 31-4, and even the $Nk/2$ contribution to the heat capacity, proved incorrect. It was reasoned that perhaps internal rotation was hindered by repulsion of the rotating groups. In ethane, the hydrogens will repel their opposites most strongly when they are directly opposed, the least when they are staggered. The repulsive potential energy is expected to vary with relative angle of rotation ϕ according to a curve shaped something like Fig. 31-1. This could be represented analytically by either of the two rather simple, one-parameter potentials,

$$U(\phi) = \tfrac{1}{2}U_0(1 - \cos 3\phi) \qquad (31\text{-}5)$$

or

$$U(\phi) = U_0 \sin^2\left(\frac{3\phi}{2}\right). \qquad (31\text{-}6)$$

The barrier height U_0 cannot be obtained from molecular quantum mechanics; it is a frightening theoretical problem. Since transitions involving internal rotation are rarely active in either the Raman or infra-red regions,

---

* Discussion and references are given by Janz, p. 26.

it is from microwave spectroscopy that values of U_0 are obtained.* Also, U_0 has been traditionally obtained by comparing theoretical results with those of macroscopic calorimetry. In that case, U_0 is a last, adjustable, catch-all parameter, and sometimes it has proved to be a surprisingly good one.

At temperatures low enough that $U_0 \gg kT$, a potential of the form of Fig. 31-1 gives a typical harmonic vibration, as shown by the dotted parabola. In that case, the internal "rotation" is simply another vibrational normal mode. The results of Sec. 19 are satisfactory. For temperatures high enough that $U_0 \ll kT$, rotation about the bond is essentially

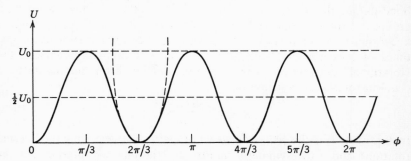

Fig. 31-1. Potential energy hindering internal rotation in ethane.

free; the parts barely feel the hindering potential. Use of Eq. 31-4 with a slight change in zero point energy is then justified.

It is for intermediate temperatures that problems arise. The interested reader is urged to consult Janz, pp. 26–34, and to work out in detail the examples presented there. Janz's notation will be clearer if Sec. 32 of this book is read first. In the case of these intermediate temperatures, the energy levels much below U_0 resemble vibrational, those much above U_0 resemble rotational levels.†

VIBRATION-ROTATION COMPLICATIONS

Use of Eqs. 19-6 and 19-18 to calculate q_{rot} and q_{vib} ignores a number of complications. As is evident from Fig. 16-2, approximating the

---

* The problems of determining barrier heights are discussed by E. B. Wilson, Jr., in *Advances in Chemical Physics*, Vol. II, I. Prigogine, Editor, Interscience Publishers, New York, 1959, p. 367.

† Another discussion of the effects of internal rotation on thermodynamic functions, complete with graphs, is given by G. Herzberg, *Infrared and Raman Spectra of Polyatomic Molecules*, D. Van Nostrand Co., New York, 1945, Sec. V,1. Most other complications in Q are also discussed.

inter-atomic energy curve in a molecule by a parabola may be reasonable for the lowest vibrational levels, but the anharmonic nature of the actual potential will introduce distortions, especially at temperatures comparable to Θ_{vib}. Furthermore, Eq. 19-6 implies that the moment of inertia of the molecule is a constant, independent of how fast the molecule is rotating or how hard it is vibrating. Yet, clearly, rotation will result in centrifugal stretching of the bond, and as the molecule vibrates its moment of inertia will change.

Corrections for these features can be made for a diatomic molecule with the introduction of several adjustable parameters by adding ϵ_{corr} to the sum of the ϵ_{rot} and ϵ_{vib} given by Eqs. 19-6 and 19-17:

$$\epsilon_{corr} = -x_e\hbar\omega(n + \tfrac{1}{2})^2 - D_e c\hbar j^2(j + 1)^2(2\pi)^{-1}$$
$$- \alpha\hbar c(n + \tfrac{1}{2})j(j + 1)(2\pi)^{-1}. \quad (32\text{-}1)$$

The term in the dimensionless quantity x_e reflects the anharmonicity of the potential. The term in D_e is from centrifugal stretching. The term in α gives the vibration-rotation interaction. Theory can relate the three parameters, x_e, D_e, and α, or they may be adjusted independently to fit experimental data.*

Two other corrections sometimes required are mentioned here. At temperatures low enough compared to Θ_{rot}, the q_{rot} obtained by integration must be corrected for the fact that the terms in the sum are discrete. Also, for some molecules the overall moment of inertia is changed in the course of internal rotation. Such a case is $H_2ClC—CH_2Cl$, which has a different overall moment of inertia when the two chlorines are next to each other than it does when they are opposed.

NUCLEAR SPIN AND SYMMETRY NUMBERS

In general, atomic nuclei have a magnetic dipole moment due to a nuclear spin angular momentum, characterized by the integral or half-integral quantum number i. Each nucleus has its nuclear spin, determined by which isotope of which element it is. Changing this spin without a profound nuclear reaction is almost impossible. The nuclear spin state has a degeneracy of $2i + 1$, and each of these $2i + 1$ states has almost identical energy.

Therefore, if nuclear spin states were to be considered, every atomic state previously considered would have to be treated as $2i + 1$ states.

* Discussions of Eq. 31-7 and the effect it makes on the partition function are given by Mayer and Mayer, pp. 160–166, and by Davidson, pp. 116–119.

Thus, Q would be multiplied by a product of factors $2i + 1$, one for each of the atoms in the system. This would modify the entropies and free energies, but would never affect *changes* in these quantities for processes not involving transmutation. Spin states essentially just change the zero of entropy and may be included in the $\overline{S_0}$ of Sec. 10. One is then justified in completely neglecting the effect of nuclear spin.

One feature in which nuclear spin is involved is the symmetry number for rotation, σ, introduced in Sec. 19. From the classical viewpoint it is easy to see why σ arises. Consider a molecule in which all *like* atoms are numbered and distinguishable. Suppose that this molecule may be rotated into σ positions which differ from each other only by the numbers labeling the like atoms. The classical rotational partition function counts the whole 4π steradians into which the molecule can rotate. Yet, if the numbered particles are truly indistinguishable, only $1/\sigma$ of the 4π steradians represent physically distinguishable alignments. Thus, for the same reason that $1/N!$ appeared in the ideal gas partition function, $1/\sigma$ is introduced into the classical limit of q_{rot}.

If this problem is approached on a strictly quantum mechanical basis, what happens is that certain of the rotational states that would otherwise appear are ruled out for reasons of symmetry. The symmetry involved arises from a combination of factors, one of which is the nuclear spin. The question of just which rotational levels are allowed and which are not is a delicate one,* and it is important at low temperatures, comparable to Θ_{rot}. The peculiar properties of ortho and para hydrogen arise from this cause.†

MISCELLANEOUS REFERENCES

Detailed corrections to thermodynamic quantities due to rotation-vibration interaction, first and second order anharmonicities, and doubly degenerate vibrations are given by H. W. Woolley, *J. Research Natl. Bur. Standards*, **56**, 105 (1956). The effect of centrifugal distortion on $\overline{G}$, $\overline{S}$, and $\overline{C_V}$ is treated by E. B. Wilson, Jr., *J. Chem. Phys.*, **6**, 526 (1936). He obtains corrections of $-\rho RT^2$, $2\rho RT$, and $2\rho RT$ respectively, where ρ is a constant (in deg^{-1}) characterizing each molecule. Examples follow: for H_2O, $\rho = 2.04 \times 10^{-5}$; for NH_3, $\rho = 1.45 \times 10^{-5}$; for C_2H_4, $\rho = 0.79 \times 10^{-5}$. The correction to $\overline{C_V}$ for water at 100°C is about $\frac{1}{2}$ per cent.

* Mayer and Mayer, pp. 135–138 and 172–178; Fowler and Guggenheim, p. 84.
† G. S. Rushbrooke, *Introduction to Statistical Mechanics*, Oxford University Press, London, 1949, pp. 100–109.

Interesting tables of the corrections to thermodynamic properties of CO_2 due to anharmonicity and vibration-rotation interaction are given by H. W. Woolley, *J. Research Natl. Bur. Standards*, **52**, 289 (1954). He also shows how the naturally occurring mixture of isotopes has different properties from $C^{12}O^{16}_2$.

32 PROBLEMS IN STATISTICAL THERMODYNAMICS

The typical problem of the chemist or engineer in statistical thermodynamics is to calculate changes in various thermodynamic quantities for processes of interest. It may be $\Delta \bar{\mu}^0$ which is desired for obtaining an equilibrium constant. Equivalent to this is knowing $\Delta \bar{G}^0$, since the molar Gibbs free energy is $N_0\mu$, and Avogadro's number times Eq. 30-10 is simply

$$\Delta \bar{G}^0 = -RT \ln \overline{K_{eq}}. \tag{32-1}$$

The chemist's rule of thumb is that if $\Delta \bar{G}^0$ is negative, the reaction is promising. If $\Delta \bar{G}^0$ is between 0 and 10 kcal, the reaction is questionable, but worth checking. If $\Delta \bar{G}^0$ is greater than 10 kcal, it is useful only under very unusual conditions. Instead of $\Delta \bar{G}^0$, it may be $\Delta \bar{H}$ which is desired in order to compute thrust in a rocket. Or it may be any of the other thermodynamic properties, needed for almost any reason. In all likelihood, one will want to know these properties over a range of interesting temperatures.

The data needed for calculating the thermodynamic properties of *gaseous* reactants and products are the following: for q_{trans} simply the molecular weight, for q_{rot} the symmetry number and moment of inertia (or product of the three principal moments of inertia in a non-linear molecule), for q_{vib} the set of fundamental frequencies of vibration of the normal modes in the molecule, for q_{elect} the degeneracy of the ground state (and information about any other electronic states with low enough energies to contribute appreciably), for q_{zero} the energy required to separate each molecule originally in its lowest energy level (or at absolute zero) into its constituent atoms. One also might want information on the vibrational anharmonicities, the centrifugal distortion, and the vibration-rotation interaction. That is all, provided the gases may be reasonably treated as ideal.

Sources of all this information are usually the following: The moment of inertia and symmetry number for either overall or internal rotation are found from a molecular model. This is usually based on electron and x-ray diffraction studies, though sometimes on spectroscopic evidence. These experiments furnish the necessary bond lengths and bond angles to construct the model. The set of fundamental vibration frequencies (with anharmonicity and centrifugal corrections and vibration-rotation interaction) comes from spectroscopy, usually Raman and infrared. The information about electronic levels comes from ultra-violet and visible spectroscopy. Most of the above information is of extraordinary precision, because spectroscopic measurements are some of science's most precise. However, the dissociation energy D_0 is obtained either from spectroscopy or calorimetry, and it is not easy to get.*

Because of the difference in precision between D_0 and the rest of the data, it is customary to use statistical mechanics first to calculate the contributions to the thermodynamic variables from the precise spectroscopic data. Where necessary, the best experimental quantity available which involves D_0 may then be used to add the final contribution. In any table of thermodynamic properties of gases, this method assures that the least precise contribution is tabulated separately where it cannot contaminate the most precisely calculated contributions.

What is done, therefore, is to tabulate *not* the Gibbs free energy and enthalpy of pure compounds at the temperature T, $\overline{G_T}^0$ and $\overline{H_T}^0$, but instead the *difference* between these quantities and $\overline{H_{T^0}}^0$. The $\overline{H_{T^0}}^0$ is the enthalpy of formation of the pure compound from its elements at a reference temperature T^0, usually either $0°K$ or $298.15°K$. As may be seen from examining Table 20-1, this procedure removes the effect of the parameters D_0 from the result but leaves in most of the effects from the spectroscopic parameters. In fact, using the zero degree enthalpy $\overline{H_0}^0$ as a base removes *only* the D_0's from the result.

The superscript ^{0} means the functions are referred to the conditions of an ideal gas at one atmosphere pressure.

It is convenient for variables being tabulated as functions of temperature to be slowly varying, thus permitting easy interpolation with a

---

* The many problems involved in determining D_0 are discussed by A. G. Gaydon, *Dissociation Energies*, Chapman and Hall, London, 2d ed., 1953.

minimum of entries. Because they are slowly varying, the so-called *enthalpy function,*

$$\frac{\overline{H_T}^0 - \overline{H_{T^0}}^0}{T} \tag{32-2}$$

and the *free energy function,*

$$-\left(\frac{\overline{G_T}^0 - \overline{H_{T^0}}^0}{T}\right) = \overline{S_T}^0 - \left(\frac{\overline{H_T}^0 - \overline{H_{T^0}}^0}{T}\right), \tag{32-3}$$

are often found in tables. Division by T makes for slower variation as a function of T. Of course, in order to find $\overline{G_T}^0$ or $\overline{H_T}^0$, the best available values of $\overline{H_{T^0}}^0$ must be tabulated too. In addition, tabulations are usually made of a specific heat and of the entropy, neither of which contain the D_0's.

It is important to understand how to calculate these quantities from the spectroscopic parameters. Sufficient theory is given in this book; the problem is one of working enough examples to become proficient. A good starting place is Example 2.1 in Janz, pp. 22-25, which may be worked out in detail. Also, Example 2.2, p. 26, is worth-while. One then is perhaps ready to study E. A. Guggenheim, *Trans. Faraday Soc.*, **37**, 97 (1941). In this paper Guggenheim gives his calculation of K_P at a number of temperatures for the reaction in which ethylene is hydrogenated to give ethane. It is interesting to work along with Guggenheim step by step as he obtains the partition function from spectral data. His calculated values of K_P are probably better than the experimental. Some helpful comments on Guggenheim's paper are given by M. Dole, *Introduction to Statistical Thermodynamics*, Prentice-Hall, New York, 1954. Also in Dole, pp. 163-170, is an interesting discussion of calculating equilibrium constants for isotopic exchange reactions. Another paper worth working through is by G. Waddington and coworkers, *J. Am. Chem. Soc.*, **71**, 797 (1949). It is interesting because it presents the thermodynamic and spectroscopic data for thiophene side by side so the results may be compared.

Once one knows how to calculate the thermodynamic functions from statistical mechanics, he may use tabulations of them with confidence and understanding. Extensive tabulations based on the most precise spectroscopic and calorimetric data available have been made. Most common inorganic compounds will be found in the compilation edited by D. R. Stull, *JANAF Interim Thermochemical Tables*, Dow Chemical Company, Midland, Michigan, 1960, This is a monumental work. It is a promising start toward a complete tabulation of the thermodynamic properties of all known compounds, which is a major goal of physical chemistry. For hydrocarbons one may consult F. Rossini, K. Pitzer,

R. Arnett, R. Braun, and G. Pimentel, editors, *Selected Values of Physical and Thermodynamic Properties of Hydrocarbons and Related Compounds*, Carnegie Press, Pittsburgh, 1953. For the elementary gaseous ions of charges $+1$ to $+4$ at temperatures of from $1000°K$ to $51,000°K$, see J. Green, D. Poland, and J. Margrave, *Thermodynamic Properties of Ions at High Temperatures*, ARL Report 191, Aeronautical Research Laboratory, Wright-Patterson Air Force Base, Ohio, 1961. A number of tables have also been made by the National Bureau of Standards.

33   FLUCTUATIONS

So far, our attention has been directed only to calculating the ensemble averages of various properties of the system. Suppose that measurements on the system give the exact value of the property being measured. We do not concern ourselves with experimental error. The ensemble averages are the values predicted by statistical mechanics for the various properties. However, most properties need not necessarily have the ensemble average value. When some property of a system deviates from its mean value (deviation from the mean defined by Eq. 4-10), this property is said to be in a *fluctuation*. Fluctuations in equilibrium systems cannot be predicted, but their relative probabilities may be computed from their occurrence in the ensemble. The likelihood of significant fluctuations is a measure of the stability of the thermodynamic properties of equilibrium systems. It is also a measure of how useful the predictions of statistical mechanics are. For example, consider the difference in usefulness to a person who knew only that 2.00 was the average value of the following sets of numbers: on the one hand, 1.98, 2.00, 2.00, 2.01, 2.01, and on the other hand, 0.10, 0.50, 1.50, 3.50, 4.40.

FLUCTUATIONS IN ENERGY

The first fluctuations considered here are those in the total energy E of a system in equilibrium with a heat bath at constant temperature.

This is an important consideration. In Part I, the canonical ensemble proved relatively easy to use in calculating averages of thermodynamic properties, so it has been tacitly assumed that all systems of interest were in contact with a heat bath and could therefore have any energy from zero to infinity. It would be nice tò prove that for a macroscopic system it makes no difference whether its properties are calculated from a canonical or a microcanonical ensemble—the probability that the energy of the system differs appreciably from $\bar{E}$ is negligible even in a canonical ensemble. Fortunately, the proof is easy. Thus, whether a system is in equilibrium with a large heat bath, a small heat bath, or nothing, its energy for a given temperature will most certainly be the same.

The ensemble average of the total energy of a system in equilibrium with a heat bath is $\bar{E}$. A good measure of the probability of significant fluctuations from $\bar{E}$ is the mean square deviation, Eq. 4-12:

$$\overline{\delta E^2} = \overline{(E - \bar{E})^2} = \overline{E^2} - \bar{E}^2. \tag{33-1}$$

Finding this is most directly done using a trick: simply differentiate the identity

$$\bar{E}Q = \sum_i E_i e^{-\beta E_i} \tag{33-2}$$

with respect to β:

$$\left(\frac{\partial \bar{E}}{\partial \beta}\right)_V Q - \bar{E} \sum_i E_i e^{-\beta E_i} = -\sum_i E_i^2 e^{-\beta E_i},$$

$$\left(\frac{\partial \bar{E}}{\partial \beta}\right)_V - \bar{E}^2 = -\overline{E^2},$$

$$\boxed{\overline{\delta E^2} = kT^2\left(\frac{\partial \bar{E}}{\partial T}\right)_V = kT^2\overline{C_V}.} \tag{33-3}$$

In the last step, use was made of the identity given in the footnote to Eq. 11-10. The mean square deviation is thus proportional to the specific heat.

Of greater interest than $\overline{\delta E^2}$ is the ratio

$$\frac{\sqrt{\overline{\delta E^2}}}{\bar{E}} = \frac{T\sqrt{k\overline{C_V}}}{\bar{E}}. \tag{33-4}$$

If this ratio is small enough, then the probability of significant deviations from $\bar{E}$ in the value of E is negligible. Both C_V and E are extensive thermodynamic variables. In general, $\overline{C_V}$ and $\bar{E}$ are approximately proportional to the number of particles contained in the system. Thus, the ratio in Eq. 33-4 varies inversely as $N^{\frac{1}{2}}$. Furthermore, the fact that the proportionality constant between Eq. 33-4 and $N^{-\frac{1}{2}}$ is not large may be seen from the case for an ideal monatomic gas. Such a gas has $\overline{C_V} = \frac{3}{2}Nk$ and $\bar{E} = \frac{3}{2}NkT$, and Eq. 33-4 becomes simply $(2/3N)^{\frac{1}{2}}$. Thus, the average amount by which one would expect the measured energy of a system to differ from $\bar{E}$ is something like $10^{-10}\bar{E}$ for macroscopic systems described by a canonical ensemble. It is inconceivable that such small fluctuations could have an effect on any property big enough to show up on measurement.

The conclusion is that *one might as well use a canonical ensemble to represent a macroscopic system, regardless of whether the system is isolated or in equilibrium with a heat bath.* Thus, one may take advantage of the relative simplicity of the canonical distribution as contrasted with the rather awkward microcanonical distribution. Of course, if the system under consideration is very small, Eq. 33-4 becomes appreciable. For example, suppose one were able to measure the energy contained in a volume V/N of about the size available to an average molecule in an ideal gas. Then Eq. 33-4 takes the value $(2/3)^{\frac{1}{2}}$. For studying such small regions, having the whole spectrum of fluctuations is of much greater importance than simply knowing $\bar{E}$. This is characteristic of a physical world made up of particles. As the regions one considers become so small that they contain a relatively few particles, the simplification arising from averaging over the chaotic motion of vast numbers of particles is lost. This is discussed further in Sec. 34, but it has been encountered before. As shown by Figs. 14-1 and 14-4, the average behavior of a *single particle* is not worth much as a prediction of what a given particle is doing.

One might ask why it is that the exponential probability, written

$$P_N(i) = e^{(\bar{A} - E_i)/kT} \tag{33-5}$$

with the aid of Eq. 11-2, leads to such a sharp peaking of probabilities around $\bar{E}$. There is nothing in Eq. 33-5 to indicate such peaking. In fact, this shows that the states of lowest energy are most probable, that as E_i approaches $\bar{A}$ the probabilities are damped, and for $E_i \gg \bar{A}$ the probabilities go to zero. The answer is that the effect of the exponential damping must be viewed together with the *number* of states available to the system in a given energy range. The quantum mechanics proves to be such that as E is increased, there is a rapid increase in the number of quantum states with energy between E and $E + dE$. The probability of finding an energy between E and $E + dE$ is the product of Eq. 33-5 and the rapidly increasing density of states. The former is exponentially damped and the latter is rising very rapidly with energy. As a result, their product gives an extremely peaked distribution in energy about the value $\bar{E}$.

FLUCTUATIONS IN PRESSURE

Another mechanical quantity whose fluctuations are of interest is the pressure. If one put a pressure measuring device into an equilibrium system, the measured instantaneous pressure might well differ from $\bar{P}$. Finding $\overline{\delta P^2}$ is completely analogous to the derivation of Eq. 33-3 from Eq. 33-2. Here one differentiates

$$\bar{P}Q = -\sum_i \left(\frac{\partial E_i}{\partial V}\right)_T e^{-E_i/kT} \tag{33-6}$$

with respect to V:

$$\left(\frac{\partial \bar{P}}{\partial V}\right)_T Q - \frac{\bar{P}}{kT}\sum_i \left(\frac{\partial E_i}{\partial V}\right)_T e^{-E_i/kT}$$

$$= -\sum_i \left(\frac{\partial^2 E_i}{\partial V^2}\right)_T e^{-E_i/kT} + \frac{1}{kT}\sum_i \left(\frac{\partial E_i}{\partial V}\right)_T^2 e^{-E_i/kT};$$

$$\left(\frac{\partial \bar{P}}{\partial V}\right)_T + \frac{\bar{P}}{kT}\bar{P} = -\overline{\left(\frac{\partial^2 E}{\partial V^2}\right)_T} + \frac{1}{kT}\overline{P^2};$$

$$\boxed{\overline{\delta P^2} = kT\left[\left(\frac{\partial \bar{P}}{\partial V}\right)_T - \overline{\left(\frac{\partial^2 E}{\partial V^2}\right)_T}\right].} \tag{33-7}$$

The analysis of Eq. 33-7 is not so simple as that of Eq. 33-3. The second term in the bracket is complicated and involves the interaction between the molecules and the instrument measuring the pressure. Fowler has shown for ideal gases that the ratio

$$\frac{\sqrt{\overline{\delta P^2}}}{\bar{P}} \tag{33-8}$$

is of order $N^{-\frac{1}{6}}$.* Therefore, the prediction one would make of the result of a pressure measurement would depend to some extent on the size of the measuring instrument and on its time response. The expectation of significant deviations from the thermodynamic pressure $\bar{P}$ increases for very small instruments with very fast response.

* R. H. Fowler, *Statistical Mechanics*, Cambridge University Press, Cambridge, 2d ed., 1936, Sec. 20–4.

THE GRAND CANONICAL ENSEMBLE

In order to study fluctuations in the numbers of molecules of various species present at equilibrium, the ensemble must be constructed so that N is a variable. This is what Gibbs called a **grand ensemble**, in contrast to a **petit ensemble**, in which the number of particles is fixed for all members. In a grand ensemble not only do members exist in each allowed quantum state for a *given* number of particles, but there are members in each allowed state for *each possible* total number of particles in the system, N_i (for the moment, consider a system containing only one kind of particle). The probability that the system will be found containing N_i particles in quantum state j is the ratio of the number of members of the ensemble containing N_i particles in quantum state j to the total number of members of the ensemble.

The problem is how to construct the explicit N-dependence of the distribution function. The system may be thought of as being "in equilibrium with a particle bath"; that is, it is open to the exchange of particles with its surroundings. The easiest way to visualize this is to think of the *system* as a relatively small but well-defined portion of a larger composite, consisting of system plus particle bath. The walls of the system are completely open to passage of the particles. The composite contains $\mathcal{N}$ particles and is in equilibrium with a heat bath, so it may be represented by a canonical distribution:

$$P_{\mathcal{N}}(i) = \frac{e^{-\beta \mathcal{E}_i}}{Q_{\mathcal{N}}}. \tag{33-9}$$

In Eq. 33-9, $P_{\mathcal{N}}(i)$ is the probability that the $\mathcal{N}$-particle composite is in its ith quantum state, which has energy $\mathcal{E}_i$. The distinction between system and particle bath is clear enough that it is meaningful to ask how many particles are in the system. Furthermore, the total energy of the composite must be expressible as the energy E of the N particles in the system in some state or other plus the energy $\mathcal{E}$ of the $\mathcal{N} - N$ particles in the bath:

$$\mathcal{E}_i = \mathcal{E} + E. \tag{33-10}$$

The probability $P(N, E)$ that the system contains N particles in a given state with energy E is simply proportional to the sum of terms of the form of Eq. 33-9,

$$P_{\mathcal{N}}(i) = e^{-\beta E} \cdot \frac{e^{-\beta \mathcal{E}}}{Q_{\mathcal{N}}}, \tag{33-11}$$

over all states of the composite which show N particles in the system in their appropriate state. It makes no difference in what state the $\mathcal{N} - N$ particles of the bath are:

$$P(N, E) \propto e^{-\beta E} \frac{\sum e^{-\beta\mathcal{E}}}{Q_\mathcal{N}} = e^{-\beta E} \frac{Q_{\mathcal{N}-N}}{Q_\mathcal{N}}, \tag{33-12}$$

$$P(N, E) \propto e^{-\beta E} \frac{Q_{\mathcal{N}-1}}{Q_\mathcal{N}} \cdot \frac{Q_{\mathcal{N}-2}}{Q_{\mathcal{N}-1}} \cdots \frac{Q_{\mathcal{N}-N}}{Q_{\mathcal{N}-N+1}}. \tag{33-13}$$

If the system is very tiny compared with the particle bath, the N ratios multiplying the exponential differ from each other by a negligible amount. Each ratio may be written as $e^{\beta\bar{\mu}}$, in complete analogy with Eq. 23-12. The result is

$$P(N_i, E_j) = \frac{1}{\Xi} e^{(N_i\bar{\mu}_i - E_j)/kT}. \tag{33-14}$$

In Eq. 33-14, $P(N_i, E_j)$ is the probability that the system contains N_i particles in quantum state j, which has energy E_j. The $\bar{\mu}_i$ is identified as the chemical potential of species i in Prob. 33-7. The reciprocal of the normalizing constant, Ξ, is called the **grand partition function**, in analogy with Q. In case there are more than one species of molecules present, each has its own particle bath and associated parameter $\bar{\mu}_i$, and the grand distribution function is

$$P(N_1, N_2, \ldots, E_j) = \frac{1}{\Xi} e^{(\Sigma_i N_i\bar{\mu}_i - E_j)/kT}. \tag{33-15}$$

The grand partition function differs from Q in involving a summation over all sets of particle numbers in addition to summing over quantum states for each set of numbers:

$$\Xi = \sum_{N_1}\sum_{N_2} \cdots \sum_j e^{(\Sigma_i N_i\bar{\mu}_i - E_j)/kT}. \tag{33-16}$$

An ensemble constructed according to Eq. 33-15 is said to be a **grand canonical ensemble**. "Grand" means that N is explicitly allowed to vary. "Canonical" reflects the fact that the members of the ensemble for any fixed value of N form a canonical ensemble among themselves. The grand canonical ensemble may be viewed as a collection of canonical ensembles, some for all different numbers of particles, weighted according to Eq. 33-15. This view recalls that given in Sec. 7 of a canonical ensemble as a collection of microcanonical ensembles of differing energies.

FLUCTUATIONS IN DENSITY

The fluctuation in number of particles of type s in the system is studied in the same way it was for energy and pressure, by differentiating

$$\overline{N_s}\Xi = \sum_{N_1}\sum_{N_2}\cdots\sum_j N_s e^{\beta(\Sigma_i N_i \overline{\mu_i} - E_j)} \tag{33-17}$$

with respect to $\overline{\mu_s}$:

$$\left(\frac{\partial \overline{N_s}}{\partial \overline{\mu_s}}\right)\Xi + \overline{N_s}\sum_{N_1}\sum_{N_2}\cdots\sum_j \beta N_s e^{\beta(\Sigma_i N_i \overline{\mu_i} - E_j)}$$

$$= \sum_{N_1}\sum_{N_2}\cdots\sum_j \beta N_s^2 e^{\beta(\Sigma_i N_i \overline{\mu_i} - E_j)};$$

$$\left(\frac{\partial \overline{N_s}}{\partial \overline{\mu_s}}\right) + \beta \overline{N_s}^2 = \beta \overline{N_s^2};$$

$$\boxed{\overline{\delta N_s^2} = \frac{kT}{(\partial \overline{\mu_s}/\partial \overline{N_s})_{T,V,\overline{N_i}\neq s}}.} \tag{33-18}$$

The value of $\overline{\delta N_s^2}$ may easily be found for an ideal gas from Eq. 30-16:

$$\overline{\mu_s} = kT \ln\frac{N_s}{q_s}; \quad \frac{\partial \overline{\mu_s}}{\partial N_s} = \frac{kT}{N_s}; \tag{33-19}$$

$$\overline{\delta N_s^2} = \overline{N_s}. \tag{33-20}$$

Therefore, for an ideal gas, the relative fluctuation is

$$\frac{\sqrt{\overline{\delta N_s^2}}}{\overline{N_s}} = \frac{1}{\sqrt{\overline{N_s}}}. \tag{33-21}$$

The same is true for fluctuations in particle densities, $\overline{\rho_s}$, since $\overline{\rho_s}$ is simply $\overline{N_s}$ divided by V.

The fluctuations about $\overline{N_s}$ are negligible for macroscopic systems. This proof helps justify use of the grand canonical ensemble to represent systems even with fixed numbers of particles. Such usage is common because many operations are simpler with the grand ensemble than with petit ensembles. For example, Sec. 30 on equilibrium constants could have been approached using a grand ensemble, though certain logical difficulties would have arisen. It is hard to visualize the "particle bath" in a closed system at chemical equilibrium. It is a source or sink for particles characterized by a constant value of the chemical potential. The fluctuations found in this section indicate the size of the fluctuations one would find about the equilibrium values of the $\overline{N}_i$ at equilibrium. Again, the simplicity and usefulness of such a concept as the equilibrium constant rests on the vast number of particles making up macroscopic systems.

It is worth noting that the relative fluctuation in particle density may be made as large as one pleases by looking in smaller and smaller volumes. Thus, as one would expect, the uniformity of density one sees in a system depends on how fine a scale one looks. That density fluctuations indeed exist in the air is testified to by the blue sky. If there were no fluctuations in density, sunlight would not be appreciably scattered and the sky would be nearly black. Small adjacent regions of greatly different densities act as scattering centers, deflecting light from its straight path near the earth. A significant density fluctuation must occur over a region whose dimensions are of the order of the wave length of the light before there is appreciable scattering. Since red light has longer wave length than blue, and since there are more significant fluctuations in small regions than large, blue light is preferentially scattered over red. Thus, the light that goes on straight is reddened, explaining in part the color of sunsets and sunrises.

We have not discussed fluctuations in temperature or entropy, because these quantities are statistical rather than mechanical. They characterize the ensemble, rather than the system; thus, in the statistical mechanical picture, they have no fluctuations. This is discussed in Sec. 34.

PROBLEMS

33-1. What value would you predict for the number of molecules in a volume of 5×10^4 Å^3 of an ideal gas at 1 atm and 300°K? Compare this with $(\overline{\delta N^2})^{1/2}$ for so small a volume. Discuss how this affects your prediction.

33-2. Contrast $(\overline{\delta F^2})^{1/2}$ with $\overline{[(\delta F)^2]^{1/2}}$, stating the meaning of each in words. Which is larger? Does the latter quantity differ from $\overline{\delta F}$? The F is an arbitrary function.

33-3. According to Sec. 29, the Debye theory of crystals gives the value $\bar{E} = 3\pi^4 N k T^4 / 5\Theta_D{}^3$ at low temperatures. Express $\overline{\delta E^2}/\bar{E}^2$ as a function of T, Θ_D, and N. In thermodynamics it is customary to consider energy and temperature as simultaneously determinable quantities, the one determining the other theoretically. Discuss this for crystals at low temperatures. For silver, $\Theta_D = 215$°K. Below what temperature does $\overline{\delta E^2}/\bar{E}^2$ exceed unity for a gram of silver (atomic weight 107.9)?

33-4. Another measure of the average of $E - \bar{E}$ in the ensemble is $\overline{\delta E^3}$. Prove that $\overline{\delta E^3} = -\partial^3 \ln Q / \partial \beta^3$.

33-5. Consider the system depicted in Fig. 33-1, in which the weight of the piston just balances the vapor pressure. What is $\overline{\delta E^2}/\bar{E}^2$ and why? What does this mean in terms of the prediction we would make of the energy of this system, knowing its temperature?

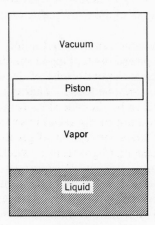

Fig. 33-1

33-6. Discuss density fluctuations in two-phase systems.

33-7. Starting with Eqs. 33-15 and 33-16, except with the $\overline{\mu_i}$ replaced by unknown parameters v_i, find $\bar{S}$ in terms of the grand partition function Ξ by a proof parallel to that of Sec. 9. Using the fact that $\bar{G} = \Sigma_i \overline{N_i \mu_i}$, prove that the v_i are indeed the chemical potentials $\overline{\mu_i}$. Also show what thermodynamic significance is attached to $kT \ln \Xi$.

34　MECHANICAL VIEW OF THERMODYNAMICS

In concluding this book, a few comments may be made pertaining to the remark made in Sec. 2 that the "explanation" of the laws of thermodynamics must lie in the mechanics of the particles comprising the system. Statistical mechanics goes a long way toward this "explanation."

It must be admitted, however, that the derivations of statistical mechanics require assumptions which are no less drastic than those of thermo-dynamics. It is assumed that the forces between particles in the system are all conservative, that is, that they may all be derived from a potential energy. Then, assuming that the energy of a state is the only function of the dynamical variables on which that state's probability may depend is a quick way to rule out numberless other things on which it just might depend. For some special models of systems, non-equilibrium statistical mechanics can prove this assumption, and it seems completely reasonable. But then, so do the laws of thermodynamics. The question of which is more "fundamental," thermodynamics or statistical mechanics, is a question each person can answer for himself.

In thermodynamics, the variables E, P, A, etc., have unique values which characterize macroscopic regions as a whole. Classical thermodynamics has no room for fluctuations, so its relationships are limited to systems large enough that fluctuations may be ignored. The relationships among these thermodynamic variables are identical to those found among the ensemble averages in statistical mechanics. One concludes that *the ensemble averages of statistical mechanics are identical to the unique values of the variables treated in thermodynamics.* We could have omitted the overbars on ensemble averages and thereby implied that these were the mechanical expressions for the thermodynamic variables.

Considering this, statistical mechanics shows clearly some of the limitations of the laws of thermodynamics. In the first place, the nice, orderly picture given by thermodynamics is valid only on a macroscopic basis. The pressure at equilibrium will most certainly be $\bar{P}$ if the measurement is over a macroscopic area. The energy found will be $\bar{E}$ if the system is macroscopic. However, on a microscopic basis, all is chaos. The *equations* for ensemble *averages* of experimental quantities may remain simple even in tiny regions, but experimental results will fluctuate wildly about the averages. If the number of particles contained in macroscopic objects were of the order of 10^3 instead of 10^{23}, things would certainly be different!

Fluctuations do not change the entropy of the system, which is determined by the constraints. They are, however, violations of any statement of the second law dealing with observable features of the behavior of matter. A simple device to harness fluctuations to violate the law is a paddle wheel, rigged so as to raise a weight if it turns clockwise, and fixed with a ratchet to prevent its turning counter-clockwise.* The pressure on the vanes of the paddle wheel arises from their bombardment by gas molecules. Over macroscopic vanes, the pressure is uniform and there is no net torque

* This illustration was suggested to the author by W. E. Vaughan of the University of Wisconsin.

However, suppose the paddle wheel could be made small enough that fluctuations would become significant. If at a given moment the fluctuating pressure on the vanes causes a counter-clockwise torque, nothing will happen. However, a fluctuation producing a large enough clockwise torque could raise the weight at the expense of the random thermal energy of the gas molecules. This is a clear violation of a corollary of Kelvin's statement of the second law.

In Sec. 33, fluctuations in entropy and temperature were not treated. The thermodynamic entropy and temperature, as calculated from statistical mechanics, are statistical quantities, not mechanical. They represent the ensemble, that is, the *information* known about the system. As such, they have unique values. The temperature arises from the partitioning of the total system energy in some unknown way into the various mechanical contributions which make up that energy. The entropy is a measure of the information one has about which quantum state an equilibrium system is in.

It is true that one may change the definitions of S and T to give them mechanical meaning. For example, one might define the temperature in an ideal gas to be $P/\rho k$, where P and ρ are the measured values of the pressure and density in a small region of the gas. This quantity would then exhibit fluctuations. One might also define the temperature as $m\overline{v^2}/3k$, where $\overline{v^2}$ is the average of the squares of the velocities of the particles in the region considered. This quantity would also exhibit fluctuations. One might even define the temperature of a particular energy contribution ϵ in a given particle by ϵ/k. Any of these or other definitions of temperature might be sanctioned by their *usefulness* in a given study. But they must not be confused with the thermodynamic temperature which comes from statistical mechanics.

The same is true of the entropy. If ΔS is defined as q_{rev}/T, then S may indeed exhibit fluctuations. Such a case is considered in Prob. 10-1. However, the entropy of statistical mechanics is a unique function of the equilibrium condition.

Even for macroscopic systems, conditions might be such that the usual thermodynamic concepts break down. In thermodynamics, the energy and temperature are thought of as determining each other. Thus for a given substance (all extra extensive variables constant, such as surface area, magnetic moment, electric moment),

$$E = E(T, V) \quad \text{or} \quad T = T(E, V). \tag{34-1}$$

In statistical mechanics if E is known, T is fixed only if the system is large enough—has enough mechanical parts contributing to the energy—that the proofs of Sec. 8 (or 22) are valid. If T is known through the system's being in equilibrium with a heat reservoir, then clearly an $\bar{E}$ is determined. However, as seen in Sec. 33, $\bar{E}$ closely determines E only for macroscopic systems, and then not at extremely low temperatures. The results of Prob. 33-3 indicate that below some low temperature, energy fluctuations become arbitrarily large even for macroscopic systems. In that case, the first of Eqs. 34-1 is invalid. Furthermore, any mechanical counterpart to temperature would be fluctuating too, along with local energy density.

Another limitation pointed up by statistical mechanics is that interaction between the system and its surroundings must be negligible. Otherwise, it would be hard to say what a state for the system is, or even how much energy belongs to the system, in contrast to the surroundings. Thermodynamics, too, is limited in this way. The energy, entropy, and related functions have very arbitrary meanings at best if the system interacts strongly with its surroundings.

One interesting curiosity arising from the statistical definition of temperature is the concept of negative temperatures. Consider a solid whose particles possess magnetic dipoles of strength μ. In a magnetic field $\mathcal{H}$ the energy of each dipole is $\mu \cdot \mathcal{H}$, and the single-particle distribution function for orientations will be proportional to $e^{-\beta \mu \cdot \mathcal{H}}$. It is possible to change the direction of $\mathcal{H}$ by 180° very quickly. The particles are now characterized by a distribution proportional to $e^{\beta \mu \cdot \mathcal{H}}$. The particles have more magnetic energy than they would have at equilibrium, but the only way they can get rid of the surplus is to give it up to vibrational modes in the crystal. It may take many seconds for this equilibration or relaxation to occur. If on a time scale short compared to the relaxation time, one were to look at only the magnetic part of the system, then one could interpret the distribution of dipoles as equilibrium but with β negative. The temperature would be negative. Of course, it is really a non-equilibrium condition which is being treated, but the coupling of the magnetic to the vibrational degrees of freedom is often so weak that negative temperatures exist for some time. As the excess energy is given up to the lattice, β is observed to become larger, go through zero, and continue getting larger until β for magnetic dipoles reaches the β of the lattice. This is the same as the temperature T decreasing from its initial negative value to $-\infty$, which is the same as $+\infty$, and then decreasing further until it reaches the temperature of the lattice.

The thermodynamic formula,

$$k\beta = \left(\frac{\partial S}{\partial E}\right)_V, \qquad (34\text{-}2)$$

also shows a negative value of β, since increasing the energy tends to align the dipoles against the field, thus driving the system to a more ordered state. This decreases the entropy. Since substances characterized by negative temperatures have excess energy compared to those with β positive, in the relaxation to true equilibrium, heat must flow from the part with β negative to the parts with β positive. Heat flows from low β to high, which is completely consistent with the theory of positive temperatures.

Here, as throughout statistical mechanics, it is natural to think of temperature in terms of β, rather than T. This is true even in thermodynamics; the natural measure of temperature is $1/kT$.

APPENDIX A: REFERENCES

d'Abro, A., *The Rise of the New Physics*, D. Van Nostrand Co., 1939, reprinted in paperback in two volumes by Dover Publications, Inc., 1951. A comprehensive work on the development of modern physics, written for the intelligent student. Long on physical intuition and mathematical conclusions; short on mathematical proofs.

Barrow, G. M., *Molecular Spectroscopy*, McGraw-Hill Book Co., New York, 1962. This book emphasizes the physical picture of the energy levels of molecules and is emminently suited for beginners.

Davidson, N., *Statistical Mechanics*, McGraw-Hill Book Co., New York, 1962. A large, modern book applying statistical mechanics to a variety of technical problems. Compare with Hill, Fowler and Guggenheim, and Mayer and Mayer.

Eisberg, R. M., *Fundamentals of Modern Physics*, John Wiley and Sons, New York, 1961. This admirable text gives an excellent presentation of basic quantum mechanics. Most of the description and some of the mathematics are suitable for beginners.

Fowler, R., **and Guggenheim,** E. A., *Statistical Thermodynamics*, Cambridge University Press, Cambridge, 1939. A large book applying statistical mechanics to a variety of problems. Formidable notation, but some discussions more thorough than found elsewhere. Compare with Davidson, Hill, and Mayer and Mayer.

Gibbs, J. W., *Elementary Principles in Statistical Mechanics*, Yale University Press, New Haven, 1902. The great work in which Gibbs ordered and unified statistical mechanics. A source of inspiration and ideas, not a text from which to learn the fundamentals.

Heitler, W., *Elementary Wave Mechanics*, Oxford University Press, London, 1945. This little book concentrates on giving a physical picture of quantum mechanics. Suitable for beginners.

Hill, T. L., *Introduction to Statistical Thermodynamics*, Addison-Wesley Publishing Co., Reading, Massachusetts, 1960. A large, modern book applying statistical mechanics to a variety of technical problems. Compare with Davidson, Fowler and Guggenheim, and Mayer and Mayer.

Hirschfelder, J. O., **Curtiss,** C. F., **and Bird,** R. B., *Molecular Theory of Gases and Liquids*, John Wiley and Sons, New York, 1954. This tome is a valuable reference for studying the application of statistical mechanics to all kinds of substances. Contains a great deal on the non-equilibrium statistical mechanics of gases.

Janz, G, J., *Estimation of Thermodynamic Properties of Organic Compounds*, Academic Press, New York, 1958. Gives a number of ways of estimating properties of complicated compounds from their known structure through statistical mechanics. Aids one's physical "feel" for the behavior of organic compounds.

Mayer, J. E., **and Mayer,** M. G., *Statistical Mechanics*, John Wiley and Sons, New York, 1940. A hard book containing much meat. A generation of scientists have been brought up on this.

Pauling, L., **and Wilson,** E. B., Jr., *Introduction to Quantum Mechanics*, McGraw-Hill Book Co., New York, 1935. Standard, classic text on basic quantum mechanics.

Pippard, A. B., *Elements of Classical Thermodynamics*, Cambridge University Press, Cambridge, 1957. A short development of the fundamentals of thermodynamics. May be sampled, read, or digested, the last not always being easy. In the author's opinion this is by far the best book on the subject.

Powell, J. I., **and Crasemann,** B., *Quantum Mechanics*, Addison-Wesley Publishing Co., Reading, Massachusetts, 1961. Modern standard text on basic quantum mechanics. Compare with Schiff.

Schiff, L. I., *Quantum Mechanics*, McGraw-Hill Book Co., New York, 2d ed., 1955. Standard text on basic quantum mechanics. Suitable for beginners only if they have some physical sophistication.

Schrödinger, E., *Statistical Thermodynamics*, Cambridge University Press, Cambridge, 2d ed., 1952, available in paperback. This little book contains many valuable ideas.

Sommerfeld, A., *Thermodynamics and Statistical Mechanics*, Academic Press, New York, 1956. It is fun to read books by the great men of science. This contains many interesting comments, including some historical.

Tolman, R. C., *The Principles of Statistical Mechanics*, Oxford University Press, London, 1938. A long, painstaking exposition of the fundamentals of classical mechanics, quantum mechanics, and statistical mechanics. For this reason, it is a very valuable reference, though difficult for the beginner.

APPENDIX B: ANSWERS AND HINTS
TO PROBLEMS

4-1. $P(i \text{ or } j) = \dfrac{n(i) + n(j) - n(i \text{ and } j)}{n} = P(i) + P(j) - P(i \text{ and } j).$

4-3. $P(i \mid j) = P(i)$; imposing the condition does not change the probability.

4-4. $P_{ij}(l_i, l_j) = P_i(l_i)P(l_j \mid l_i) = P_j(l_j)P(l_i \mid l_j).$

4-5. The proof follows that of Eq. 4-9:

$$\bar{h} = \sum_{l_1} \sum_{l_2} \cdots \sum_{l_s} P(l_1, l_2, \ldots, l_s) h(l_1, l_2, \ldots, l_s);$$

$$\bar{h} = \iint \cdots \int dl_1 \, dl_2 \cdots dl_s f_{1,2,\ldots,s}(l_1, l_2, \ldots, l_s) h(l_1, l_2, \ldots, l_s).$$

4-6. $f_{3,4}(l_3, l_4) = \displaystyle\int dl_1 \, dl_2 \, dl_5 \, dl_6 f_{1,2,\ldots,6}(l_1, l_2, \ldots, l_6);$

$f_{1,3,6}(l_1, l_3, l_6) = \displaystyle\int dl_2 \, dl_4 \, dl_5 f_{1,2,\ldots,6}(l_1, l_2, \ldots, l_6);$

$\bar{h} = \displaystyle\int dl_1 \, dl_2 \cdots dl_6 f_{1,2,\ldots,6}(l_1, l_2, \ldots, l_6) h(l_2, l_3, l_5);$

$\bar{h} = \displaystyle\int dl_2 \, dl_3 \, dl_5 f_{2,3,5}(l_2, l_3, l_5) h(l_2, l_3, l_5).$

4-7. From $P_{ij}(l_i, l_j)$ one may obtain not only $P_i(l_i)$ and $P_j(l_j)$ but also $P(l_i \mid l_j)$ and $P(l_j \mid l_i)$. Thus, P_{ij} gives the relative number of members of the ensemble having both l_i and l_j simultaneously, while P_i and P_j together do not. They can *never* furnish as much information as P_{ij}, because even when i and j are uncorrelated, that fact is not implied by the P_i and P_j unless $P_{ij} = P_i P_j$ is given.

6-1. $1/\mathcal{N}$. Use normalization condition.

10-1. It would have had to show zero residual entropy, because the experiment has no way of knowing what the experimenter knows or does not know. Yes, more heat would be required, though only a *very little* would do, since T is so low and $\delta q/T$ is the important quantity. The excess heat could compensate for the difference between the lowest energy levels of the completely ordered and the random states. Entropies should nevertheless be reproducible because there are only a very few ordered states available compared to an enormous number of disordered ones. The odds are fantastically against the system's being in such a remarkable state. It is possible, however. See Secs. 33 and 34.

13-1. *Hint:* Let the desired integral $I = \int_{-\infty}^{\infty} dx \, e^{-ax^2}$. Since the name given the dummy integration variable is unimportant,

$$I = \int_{-\infty}^{\infty} dy \, e^{-ay^2}$$

also. Thus $I^2 = \int_{-\infty}^{\infty} \int_{-\infty}^{\infty} dx \, dy \, e^{-a(x^2+y^2)}$. This may be viewed as an integral over a two-dimensional surface and integrated easily after being put into polar coordinates. Knowledge of this trick is a source of pride to many people.

13-2. *Hint:* Consider the second derivative with respect to a of Eq. C-1.

13-3. *Hint:* Consider the first derivative with respect to a of Eq. C-1.

13-4. *Hint:* $p^2 = p_x^2 + p_y^2 + p_z^2$. It is especially interesting to note that because the three momentum components are dummy integration variables, the average of p_x^2 is the same as that of p_y^2 and the same as that of p_z^2, and each contributes $\frac{1}{2}kT$ to $\bar{\epsilon}_{\text{trans}}$. This is elaborated in Sec. 16.

14-2. Consider the derivative with respect to a of Eq. C-2.

14-3. $v_{1\,\text{rms}}/v_{2\,\text{rms}} = \bar{v}_1/\bar{v}_2 = v_{1\,\text{mp}}/v_{2\,\text{mp}} = (m_2/m_1)^{1/2}$. In this case, answer is 4.

14-4. 1.78×10^5 cm/sec, 4.75×10^4 cm/sec. These are of the same orders of magnitude as the velocities of sound in these gases.

14-5. *Hint:* Consider what is meant by $\phi(v) \, dv$.

Answer:

$$\frac{2\pi}{(\pi kT)^{3/2}} e^{-\kappa/kT}\kappa^{1/2} \, d\kappa. \qquad \kappa_{mp} = \frac{kT}{2}.$$

Why is $\frac{1}{2}mv_{mp}^2$ not equal to $\mathscr{H}_{mp}$?

14-7. *Hint:* The equation $\lambda = \lambda_0(1 + v_z/c)$ may be solved for v_z. Since the observer sees from only one direction, one starts with Eq. 14-6, using the fact that $\Phi(v_z) \, dv_z$ times I is the radiation seen by molecules whose z component of velocity lies between v_z and $v_z + dv_z$. From this, the proof is easy that

$$I(\lambda) = \frac{Ic}{\lambda_0}\left(\frac{m}{2\pi kT}\right)^{1/2} e^{-mc^2(\lambda-\lambda_0)^2/2\lambda_0^2 kT}.$$

This is sometimes written in the form

$$I(\lambda) = I(\lambda_0)e^{-mc^2(\lambda-\lambda_0)^2/2\lambda_0^2 kT}. \qquad \text{Why?}$$

14-8. erf $2 = 0.9953$.

14-9. See the paragraph before the summary in Sec. 8. In particular, what would happen to the high energy tails of the curve?

14-10. 0.349 km/sec compared with 0.421 km/sec.

15-1. 34.2 Å. 2860 Å.

15-2. 3.22×10^5. 14,600 meters.

15-3. *Hint:* Consider the part of Eq. 15-16 which involves integration over momenta. If you put the volume element in momentum space in spherical coordinates, what integral leads to the desired result?

15-4. $(\pi N/V)(m/2\pi kT)^{3/2}v^3 \, dv \, e^{-mv^2/2kT}$. The hint is the same as for Prob. 15-3.

15-5. $2(kT/m)^{1/2}$. $\overline{KE} = 2kT$, compared with $3kT/2$. A greater fraction of the faster molecules are able to effuse through the hole.

15-6. Effusion of H_2 is proportional to $P_{H_2}M_{H_2}^{-1/2}$; effusion of O_2 is proportional to $P_{O_2}M_{O_2}^{-1/2}$. Thus, H_2 molecules effuse 0.707/0.354 or twice as fast into the O_2 as the O_2 molecules effuse into the H_2.

15-7. 1.8×10^{18}.

15-8. $2^{-3/4}A/s$.

15-9. Dividing the answer to Prob. 15-3 by Eq. 15-8 gives the probability that the molecule hits the plane at an angle from the normal of between θ and $\theta + d\theta$. The average distance from the plane may be seen from a diagram to be $L \overline{\cos \theta}$, and $\overline{\cos \theta}$ is found by integration to be 2/3.

16-1. (a) $3R/2$, (b) $7R/2$, (c) $6R$, (d) $13R/2$, (e) $12R$.

17-1. Total terms in $q^N = 27{,}000$. Terms with triple occupancy $= 20$. Terms with double occupancy $= 6 \times (19 + 18 + 17 + 16 + \cdots) = 6 \times 190 = 1140$. Fraction with multiple occupancy $= 1160/27{,}000 = 0.043$. If N were larger, a value of $r = 10$ would make this fraction decrease severely.

17-2. Fermions: states—$H\text{-}T$ only; therefore $P(H\text{-}T) = 1$, $P(H\text{-}H) = 0$. Bosons: states—$H\text{-}H$, $H\text{-}T$, $T\text{-}T$; therefore $P(H\text{-}T) = \frac{1}{3}$, $P(H\text{-}H) = \frac{1}{3}$. Distinguishable: states—$H\text{-}H$, $H\text{-}T$, $T\text{-}H$, $T\text{-}T$; therefore $P(H\text{-}T$ or $T\text{-}H) = \frac{1}{2}$, $P(H\text{-}H) = \frac{1}{4}$. Boltzmann statistics gives the same probabilities as found for distinguishable particles. Boltzmann statistics differs in using a different partition function for calculating thermodynamic variables. It would be inappropriate in this case.

18-2. Ratio $= e^{(3\pi^2\hbar^2/2ma^2kT)} = e^{(9 \times 10^{-19})} \approx 1$. The energy difference between successive levels is infinitesimal compared to kT. Note that there are three states with the higher level and only one with the lower, so there are three times as many particles in the higher *energy level* as in the lowest. *Hint in obtaining answer:* see end of Sec. 8.

18-3. $\overline{S}_{\text{trans}} = Nk \ln \left[eV \left(\dfrac{mkT}{2\pi\hbar^2} \right)^{3/2} \right]$.

$\bar{\mu}_{\text{trans}} = -kT \ln \left[V \left(\dfrac{mkT}{2\pi\hbar^2} \right)^{3/2} \right]$.

18-5. About $4°\text{K}$, which is approximately the temperature of liquefaction of helium.

19-1. (a) 1, (b) 3, (c) 7, (d) 9.

19-3. $\left(\displaystyle\int_{T/\Theta_{\text{rot}}}^{\infty} dz \, e^{-z\Theta_{\text{rot}}/T} \right) \Big/ \left(\displaystyle\int_{0}^{\infty} dz \, e^{-z\Theta_{\text{rot}}/T} \right) = e^{-1}$.

19-4. Ratio $= e^{\Theta_{\text{vib}}/T}$. In this case, ratio $= e^{3340/298} = 7.4 \times 10^4$. *Note:* This is the constant ratio of populations for *each* successive vibrational level to the one below it.

19-5. Ratio $= \dfrac{e^0}{(2+1)e^{-(1)(2)\Theta_{\text{rot}}/T}} = \dfrac{e^{2\Theta_{\text{rot}}/T}}{3}$.

In this case, ratio $= 0.34$. *Note:* This is *not* a constant ratio.

19-8. *Hint:* In expanding the exponential in the denominator of the second term in Eq. 19-23, three terms must be taken.

20-1. $\bar{A} = -kT \ln (1 + e^{-\epsilon/kT})$; $\bar{E} = \epsilon e^{-\epsilon/kT}/(1 + e^{-\epsilon/kT})$;

$$\bar{S} = k \ln{(1 + e^{-\epsilon/kT})} + \epsilon e^{-\epsilon/kT}/T(1 + e^{-\epsilon/kT});$$

$$\overline{C_V} = \epsilon^2 e^{\epsilon/kT}/kT^2(e^{\epsilon/kT} + 1)^2.$$

The hump in the curve about $T = \epsilon/2k$ is characteristic of the thawing out of energy levels. It is often observed experimentally, and has been called the *Shottky anomaly*.

20-2. Incorporating a new zero of energy $\mathscr{E}$ contributes $\mathscr{E}/kT$ to $\ln Q$. Thus $\partial \ln Q/\partial\mathscr{E} = 1/kT$. It is easy to show that the derivative with respect to $\mathscr{E}$ of any of the quantities mentioned is zero, since $\partial/\partial\mathscr{E}$ may be interchanged in order of application with any of the other derivatives.

20-3. Slide rule accuracy should yield about 30 cal/deg-mole. If the most precise values of all constants are used, the result is 30.126 cal/deg-mole, which is precisely the experimental value.

20-5. A review of the argument leading to $Q = q^N/N!$ for one-component gases will show the way to a proof that in this case $Q = q_a{}^{N_a}q_b{}^{N_b}/N_a! \, N_b!$

20-6. Different gases: $\Delta\bar{S} = N_a k \ln\left(\dfrac{V_a + V_b}{V_a}\right) + N_b k \ln\left(\dfrac{V_a + V_b}{V_b}\right).$

Same gases:

$$\Delta\bar{S} = N_a k \ln\left[\left(\frac{V_a + V_b}{N_a + N_b}\right)\left(\frac{N_a}{V_a}\right)\right] + N_b k \ln\left[\left(\frac{V_a + V_b}{N_a + N_b}\right)\left(\frac{N_b}{V_b}\right)\right].$$

Note: The "entropy of mixing," as usually defined in thermodynamics, is based on the fact that identical molecules are indistinguishable, and their interchange does not lead to a new quantum state.

20-7. In complete analogy with the three-dimensional case:

$$Q_{\text{trans}} = \frac{q_{\text{trans}}^N}{N!} = \frac{(mkT\mathscr{A}/2\pi\hbar^2)^N}{N!}$$

$$\bar{\mathscr{P}} = kT\left(\frac{\partial \ln Q}{\partial\mathscr{A}}\right)_{T,N}; \qquad \bar{\mathscr{P}}\mathscr{A} = NkT.$$

20-8. $q_{\text{elect}} = 2\sum_{n=1}^{\infty} e^{\beta a/n^2} < 2\sum_{n=1}^{\infty} 1 = \infty.$

Thus, $q_{\text{elect}} = \infty$, and $e^{\beta a/n^2}/q_{\text{elect}} = 0$ for *any* state, *even the ground state*. This is delightful. *Hint:* see Hirschfelder, Curtiss, and Bird, pp. 268–271. Also see Prob. 30-5.

20-9. What happens when an appreciable amount of electronic excitation occurs?

21-1. -0.0114 atm.

21-2. 57 km. 10^{39}.

21-3. 5500 m. *Note:* The *average* height of a particle is harder to find and is about 8000 m. It would be infinity if the correct gravitational potential were used (!).

21-4. *Hint:* $\rho(r) = Ae^{(m\omega^2 r^2/2kT)}$, which need only be normalized to give N molecules in the volume V.

Answer:

$$\rho(r) = \frac{Nm\omega^2 e^{m\omega^2 r^2/2kT}}{2\pi kTl(e^{m\omega^2 R^2/2kT} - 1)}.$$

21-5. 6.9×10^{23} mole^{-1}.

23-2. $\bar{\mu} < 0$. *Hint:* $\overline{N_i}$ must be positive for all states i, even in the case $\epsilon_i = 0$.

24-1. Zero. *Hint:*

$$\sum_i \ln (1 + e^{(\bar{\mu}_0 - \epsilon_i)/kT}) = \sum_{\substack{i \\ \epsilon_i > \bar{\mu}_0}} \ln 1 + \sum_{\substack{i \\ \epsilon_i < \bar{\mu}_0}} \ln (1 + e^{(\bar{\mu}_0 - \epsilon_i)/kT}),$$

and in the second term the unity may be neglected compared to the huge exponential.

25-3. Compare Eq. 25-16 with twice Eq. 25-15. Photons greater: $\omega < 0.69kT/\hbar$. States greater: $\omega > 0.69kT/\hbar$. For $\omega \gg 0.69kT/\hbar$, the unity in the parenthesis of the denominator of Eq. 25-17 may be neglected. The result then is the same as the use of Boltzmann statistics, Eq. 22-20, would give. *Note:* For radiation it is *low* temperatures which give an appreciable fraction of frequencies satisfactorily described by Boltzmann statistics.

27-1. $B(T) = \frac{2}{3}\pi\sigma^3[1 - (e^{\beta\epsilon} - 1)(R^3 - 1)]$. What effect makes $B(T)$ larger and positive? What makes $B(T)$ smaller or even negative?

27-2. At $r = 2.71\sigma$, U_{ij} has risen to $-\epsilon/100$.

27-3. $B' = B$; $C' = (C - B^2)/kT$.

27-5. $\bar{\mathscr{P}} = \dfrac{NkT}{\mathscr{A}} - \dfrac{N^2 kT}{2\mathscr{A}^2} \displaystyle\int_0^\infty 2\pi r \, dr(e^{-U(r)/kT} - 1)$.

28-1. The same as for van der Waals' equation. The only difference lies with the higher virial coefficients, so the question of which is better is more a matter of luck than of theory.

28.2. $b =$ four times the volume of a hard sphere molecule. *Hint:* Use Eq. 28-6 and remember that r is the distance between *centers* of two molecules.

28-3. $T_c = 8a/27kb$; $V_c = 3Nb$; $P_c = a/27b^2$.

28-4. $\left(P_R + \dfrac{3}{V_R{}^2}\right)(V_R - \tfrac{1}{3}) = \tfrac{8}{3}T_R$.

Note: The parameters a and b have vanished into the critical point variables, on which the dimensionless or reduced variables are based. In terms of reduced variables, all gases behave in the same way. See Sec. 31.

28-5. $\left(P + \dfrac{N^2a}{V^2}\right)\left(V - Nb - \dfrac{Nc}{k^2T^2}\right) = NkT$

or

$\left(P + \dfrac{N^2a}{V^2} - \dfrac{N^2c}{V^2kT}\right)(V - Nb) = NkT.$

Compare with the Berthelot and the Beattie-Bridgeman equations of state discussed by Hirschfelder, Curtiss, and Bird, Sec. 4-2.

29-1. $\tfrac{12}{5}\pi^4 Nk(T/\Theta_D)^3$.

29-3. $\alpha = \left(\dfrac{\partial \Theta_D}{\partial P}\right)_T \left[\dfrac{12Nk}{V\Theta_D} D\left(\dfrac{\Theta_D}{T}\right) - \dfrac{9Nk}{VT(e^{\Theta_D/T} - 1)}\right].$

High temperatures:

$$\alpha = \frac{\overline{C_V}}{V}\left(\frac{\partial \ln \omega_{max}}{\partial P}\right)_T.$$

Hints: Recall one of the Maxwell relations from thermodynamics; use Eqs. 29-28 and C-10.

30-1. $N_i = V\rho_i$, so $\rho_1{}^{v_1}\rho_2{}^{v_2}\rho_3{}^{v_3}\cdots = q_1{}^{v_1}q_2{}^{v_2}q_3{}^{v_3}\cdots V^{-\Delta v}.$

30-2. $\dfrac{\rho_A\rho_B}{\rho_{AB}} = \dfrac{(q_A/V)(q_B/V)}{q_{AB}/V}$

$= \left\{\left(\dfrac{m_A kT}{2\pi\hbar^2}\right)^{3/2} g_{0,A} \left(\dfrac{m_B kT}{2\pi\hbar^2}\right)^{3/2} g_{0,B}\right\} \div \left\{\left[\dfrac{(m_A + m_B)kT}{2\pi\hbar^2}\right]^{3/2}\right.$

$$\times \left(\frac{T}{\Theta_{\text{rot}}}\right)\left[\frac{e^{-\Theta_{\text{vib}}/2T}}{1 - e^{-\Theta_{\text{vib}}/T}}\right]g_{0,\text{AB}}e^{(D_0/kT + \Theta_{\text{vib}}/2T)}\Bigg\}$$

$$= \left[\frac{m_\text{A}m_\text{B}kT}{(m_\text{A} + m_\text{B})2\pi\hbar^2}\right]^{3/2}\left(\frac{\Theta_{\text{rot}}}{T}\right)(1 - e^{-\Theta_{\text{vib}}/T})\left(\frac{g_{0,\text{A}}g_{0,\text{B}}}{g_{0,\text{AB}}}\right)e^{-D_0/kT}.$$

Note particularly how the dissociation energy enters the denominator in q_{zero} as a correction for the different zero of energy in the conventional q_{AB}. For temperatures below Θ_{vib}, this is proportional to $\sqrt{T}e^{-\epsilon/kT}$, and so increases with temperature. For very high temperatures this becomes proportional to $(T)^{-1/2}$, and so decreases with temperature, which is unreasonable. The assumption of an infinite number of evenly spaced vibrational levels of course breaks down. There can only be a finite number of levels in a potential well of finite depth. The same holds for rotational levels, because if too much rotational energy is present, centrifugal force will break the chemical bond.

30-3. Essentially identical, except that the symmetry number, 2, for A_2 makes the equilibrium constant twice as big.

30-4. $\dfrac{\rho_\text{A^+}\rho_{e^-}}{\rho_\text{A}} \approx \dfrac{2g_{0,\text{A}^+}}{g_{0,\text{A}}}\left(\dfrac{m_e kT}{2\pi\hbar^2}\right)^{3/2}e^{-\epsilon^0/kT}.$

30-5. Let $x = T/\Theta_{\text{ion}}$. Then 10^{20} cm$^{-3} \approx 2(m_e\text{-}\epsilon^0/2\pi\hbar^2)^{3/2}x^{3/2}e^{-1/x}$; $e^{1/x} \approx 2470x^{3/2}$, the solution of which is about 0.16. This is most easily found by letting $z = 1/x$ and solving $z = 9.02 - 3.45 \log z$ by trial and error. Thus most of the atoms are ionized at temperatures small compared to Θ_{ion}. Since excited *electronic* levels in most atoms are of the same order as ϵ^0, the use of ground electronic energies is justified even under conditions of extreme ionization. This is especially true at densities lower than the rather high $10^{20}/\text{cm}^3$ chosen for this problem. See Prob. 20-8.

30-6. $\alpha = \dfrac{\rho_\text{H^+}}{\rho_\text{H}{}^0} \approx \dfrac{\rho_\text{H^+}}{\rho_\text{H}} = \dfrac{\rho_{e^-}}{\rho_\text{H}}$,

$$\frac{\rho_\text{H^+}\rho_{e^-}}{\rho_\text{H}} \approx \rho_\text{H}{}^0\alpha^2 = \frac{2g_{0,\text{A}^+}}{g_{0,\text{A}}}\left(\frac{m_e kT}{2\pi\hbar^2}\right)^{3/2}e^{-\epsilon^0/kT}; \qquad \alpha = 7.7 \times 10^{-3}.$$

30-7. $K = \left(\dfrac{m_\text{HCl}}{m_{\text{H}_2}}\right)^{3/2}\left(\dfrac{m_\text{HCl}}{m_{\text{Cl}_2}}\right)^{3/2}\left(\dfrac{4\Theta_{\text{rot},\text{H}_2}\Theta_{\text{rot},\text{Cl}_2}}{\Theta^2_{\text{rot},\text{HCl}}}\right)[e^{(2D_{0,\text{HCl}}-D_{0,\text{H}_2}-D_{0,\text{Cl}_2})/kT}]$

$$\times \left[\frac{(1 - e^{-\Theta_{\text{vib},\text{H}_2}/T})(1 - e^{-\Theta_{\text{vib},\text{Cl}_2}/T})}{(1 - e^{-\Theta_{\text{vib},\text{HCl}}/T})^2}\right] \approx 6.3 \times 10^9.$$

33-1. From ideal gas law, $\bar{N} = PV/kT = 1.23$. $\overline{\delta N^2} = \sqrt{\bar{N}} = 1.11$.

33-2. $\overline{[(\delta F)^2]^{1/2}} = \overline{|\delta F|}$ and is smaller because greater values receive less weight in the averaging.

33-3. $\overline{\delta E^2}/\bar{E}^2 = 20\Theta_D{}^3/3\pi^4 N T^3$. $T = 4.95 \times 10^{-6}$ deg. *Note:* The highest known value of Θ_D is for carbon, about ten times that given for silver.

33-4. *Hint:* Recall that

$$\bar{E} = -\frac{1}{Q}\frac{\partial Q}{\partial \beta}, \quad \overline{E^2} = \frac{1}{Q}\frac{\partial^2 Q}{\partial \beta^2}, \quad \overline{E^3} = -\frac{1}{Q}\frac{\partial^3 Q}{\partial \beta^3}.$$

33-5. This is a good example of a case in which knowledge of T does not imply knowledge of E. *Hint:* Gibbs (p. 75) was the first to realize that this result both followed from statistical mechanics and was true experimentally.

33-6. *Hints:* How does μ change when particles are added to a two-phase system? How are the fluctuations observed? *Note:* Also, for a system at its *critical point*, addition of more particles does not change μ, and widespread fluctuations are expected. The extraordinary light scattering ability of liquids at their critical point attests to this.

33-7. Where $\ln Q$ was a function of β and V, $\ln \Xi$ is a function of β, V, the N_i, and the ν_i. In this case, $\partial \ln \Xi/\partial \beta = \sum_i N_i \nu_i - \bar{E}$. The procedure of Sec. 9 yields

$$\boxed{\bar{S} = k \ln \Xi - \frac{\sum_i \overline{N_i}\nu_i}{T} + \frac{\bar{E}}{T}.}$$

Then if $\bar{G} = \bar{E} + \bar{P}V - T\bar{S} = \sum_i \overline{N_i}\mu_i$, $\bar{E} + \bar{P}V - kT \ln \Xi + \sum_i \overline{N_i}\nu_i - \bar{E} = \sum_i \overline{N_i}\mu_i$. Thus, $\boxed{\nu_i = \overline{\mu_i}}$ and $\boxed{\bar{P}V = kT \ln \Xi.}$

APPENDIX C: DEFINITE INTEGRALS

$$\int_{-\infty}^{\infty} dz\, e^{-az^2} = 2\int_0^{\infty} \cdots = 2\int_{-\infty}^0 \cdots = \frac{\pi^{1/2}}{a^{1/2}} \qquad \text{(C-1)}$$

$$\int_0^{\infty} dz\, ze^{-az^2} = \int_{-\infty}^0 dz\, |z|\, e^{-az^2} = \frac{1}{2a} \qquad \text{(C-2)}$$

$$\int_{-\infty}^{\infty} dz\, z^2 e^{-az^2} = 2\int_0^{\infty} \cdots = 2\int_{-\infty}^0 \cdots = \frac{\pi^{1/2}}{2a^{3/2}} \qquad \text{(C-3)}$$

$$\int_0^{\infty} dz\, z^3 e^{-az^2} = \frac{1}{2a^2} \qquad \text{(C-4)}$$

$$\int_{-\infty}^{\infty} dz\, z^4 e^{-az^2} = 2\int_0^{\infty} \cdots = 2\int_{-\infty}^0 \cdots = \frac{3\pi^{1/2}}{4a^{5/2}} \qquad \text{(C-5)}$$

$$\int_0^{\infty} dz\, z^5 e^{-az^2} = \frac{1}{a^3} \qquad \text{(C-6)}$$

$$\int_0^{\infty} dz\, e^{-az} = \frac{1}{a} \qquad \text{(C-7)}$$

$$\int_0^{\infty} dz\, ze^{-az} = \frac{1}{a^2} \qquad \text{(C-8)}$$

$$\int_0^{\infty} \frac{dz\, z^3}{e^z - 1} = \frac{\pi^4}{15} \qquad \text{(C-9)}$$

$$\frac{d}{dx} \int_0^x f(z)\, dz = f(x) \qquad \text{(C-10)}$$

$$\int_0^x \ln(1 - e^{-z})z^2\, dz = \frac{x^3}{3} \ln(1 - e^{-x}) - \int_0^x \frac{z^3\, dz}{3(e^z - 1)} \qquad \text{(C-11)}$$

APPENDIX D: GLOSSARY OF SYMBOLS, VALUES OF CONSTANTS

Numbers in parentheses refer to equations in which symbols are first used or thoroughly defined. Symbols that appear infrequently or in one section only are not listed.

A = Helmholtz free energy (11-1)

Å = Angstrom unit, 10^{-8} cm

$B(T)$ = second virial coefficient (27-21)

c = velocity of light in vacuum, 3.00×10^{10} cm/sec

C_P = heat capacity of system at constant pressure (11-9)

C_V = heat capacity of system at constant volume (11-9)

D_0 = energy needed to ionize a molecule in its lowest vibrational state, Fig. 16-2

E = internal energy of the macroscopic system

e = base of natural logarithms, 2.72

E_i = energy of macroscopic system in its ith quantum state (6-1)

f_1 = one-particle distribution function (13-1)

f_N = complete distribution function (26-1)

G = Gibbs free energy of system (11-8)

g = acceleration of gravity, 980 cm/sec²

g_i = degeneracy of the ith energy level (8-9)

g_0 = degeneracy of the lowest electronic energy level

H = enthalpy of system (11-7)

$\hbar$ = Planck's constant divided by 2π, $\hbar = 1.054 \times 10^{-27}$ erg-sec

I = moment of inertia of molecule (19-6)

j = rotational quantum number (19-6)

k = Boltzmann's constant, 1.38×10^{-16} erg/deg = 1.36×10^{-22} cm³-atm/deg

K_{eq} = equilibrium constant (30-13)

L = mean free path (15-13)

M = molecular weight

m = mass of a particle

N = number of particles in system

n = vibrational quantum number (19-17)

$\mathbf{n}$ = vector in quantum number space, Fig. 18-1

N_i = number of particles of type i in system (11-3)

$\overline{N_i}$ = occupation number of particle state i, Sec. 22

N_0 = Avogadro's number, 6.02×10^{23}/mole

P = thermodynamic pressure (11-4)

p = magnitude of the vector $\mathbf{p}$

$\mathbf{p}$ = momentum vector for a particle (13-3)

$P_N(i)$ = probability the N-particle system is in the ith quantum state (6-1)

p_x = x component of momentum $\mathbf{p}$

Q = partition function for the system (9-3)

q = heat absorbed by system

q = partition function for a single particle (17-2)

Q_N = same as Q with number of particles noted explicitly (22-2)

R = universal gas constant, 1.99 cal/deg-mole = 8.314×10^7 erg/deg-mole

r = magnitude of the vector $\mathbf{r}$

$\mathbf{r}$ = position vector locating the center of mass of a particle (13-3)

$\mathbf{r}_{ij}$ = position of particle i relative to particle j (27-10)

S = entropy of system

s_{21} = collision cross-section, Fig. 15-1

T = absolute temperature

U_{ij} = intermolecular potential energy between particles i and j (26-14)

V = volume of system

v = magnitude of the vector $\mathbf{v}$

$\bar{v}$ = average speed of a particle (14-11)

$\mathbf{v}$ = velocity vector for a particle (14-3)

$\mathbf{v}_{21}$ = velocity of particle 2 relative to that of particle 1 (15-1)

v_{mp} = most probable speed of a particle (14-9)

v_{rms} = root mean square speed of a particle (14-14)

v_x = x component of velocity v

w = work done by system

x = rectangular coordinate

y = rectangular coordinate

z = rectangular coordinate

Z_1 = collision frequency for a particle (15-12)

β = $1/kT$

Γ_N = particle flux due to effusion (15-18)

ϵ = energy of a small part of the system (7-2)

ϵ_{trans} = translational energy of a particle (13-11)

Θ = characteristic temperature of degeneration (24-3)

Θ_D = Debye characteristic temperature (29-21)

Θ_E = Einstein characteristic temperature (29-8)

Θ_{rot} = characteristic temperature of rotation (19-7)

Θ_{trans} = characteristic temperature of translation (18-12)

Θ_{vib} = characteristic temperature of vibration (19-18)

μ = molecular chemical potential or molecular Gibbs free energy (11-4)

ν_i = stoichiometric number of species i (30-1)

ρ = particle density, particles/unit volume

σ = symmetry number for rotation (19-9)

Φ = distribution function for one component of velocity (14-6)

ϕ = one-particle distribution function for molecular speeds (14-8)

Φ_1 = one-particle velocity distribution function (14-5)

φ_1 = one-particle momentum distribution function (14-1)

ω = angular velocity in radians/sec; sometimes called *frequency*

INDEX